Australian Travelers Backpacking Guide :

the most comprehensive directory of hostels & cheap accommodation for backpackers travel across Australia

"Australian Travelers Backpacking Guide," by Leo Jahaan.
ISBN 1-58939-425-9.

Published 2003 by Virtualbookworm.com Publishing Inc., P.O. Box 9949, College Station, TX, 77842, US. ©2003 Leo Jahaan. All rights reserved. No part of this publication may be reproduced, stored in a retrieval system, or transmitted in any form or by any means, electronic, mechanical, recording or otherwise, without the prior written permission of Leo Jahaan.

Manufactured in the United States of America.

Contents

Useful Information

Welcome!

Congratulations on making the decision to visit one of the most spectacularly beautiful and diverse countries in the world. We hope you will take the time to read all the sections in this introduction, to learn how things work in Australia and plan for a hassle-free journey. Australia is a very large country, so if you only have a short time then you will need to plan your trip to see the most. Australians are renowned for their friendliness, and the staff of most hostels will go out of their way to make you feel at home and show you everything that Australia has to offer. When backpackers finish their journey around Australia and are departing for home or onward travel, they have a single common thought – "I can't wait to get back to Australia again!"

The vast majority of accommodation in this book goes by the classification of 'hostel', although that word is now often being replaced by the word 'backpackers'. It's usually true that in life you get what you pay for – but that often isn't the case with backpackers accommodation. Hostels offer the cheapest low-budget places for you to stay while traveling, yet in many ways hostels offer backpackers far more than if they were to stay in more expensive hotels. Many hostels feature very fun and social lounges, internet cafes, bars and restaurants, entertainment, travel and tour bookings, and more.

There is one thing in common between the various hostels in this book - they virtually all offer the opportunity to share your room with strangers! Dorm rooms may have as little as 3 or as many as 16 beds in one room, with the average usually being around 6 to 8 beds. Costs have not been listed in this book because they tend to change often due to current conditions and seasons, but as a rough guide you'll usually pay between AU$15 to $25 for a dorm room (that's Australian Dollars, and if you're from the U.S.A or Europe your money will go a lot further in Australia). Sometimes female-only dorms are available, although mixed rooms are virtually always safe and fun. Sheets and blankets are almost always available, sometimes with a small fee but very often free. Many hostels also offer double or single rooms, with prices ranging from around AU$30 to $60.

Many hostels in Australia belong to one or more of the 3 major hostel chains – VIP, Nomads, and YHA. Other hostels are independent of the major chains. Each of the chain's management would probably like to convince you that their hostels have higher standards than their competitors. In reality, every hostel in Australia is usually managed completely independently of any other hostel, so each has it's own positive qualities, unique atmosphere, etc. However each chain does offer relatively inexpensive membership to backpackers, which will usually give you accommodation discounts at every hostel in the chain. The amount of the discount varies, although even a discount of only $1 per night will often make membership worthwhile if you're staying in Australia for more than a month. Although most discount cards are available for purchase once you arrive, YHA membership is only available for purchase through the International Youth Hostel Federation in your **home country** before you arrive. For more information visit their web-site at *www.hihostels.com*

If you find any information in this book has changed or is no longer relevant, please feel free to inform us by email or through our web-site so that changes can be made for future editions of the book. By visiting our web-site you can also keep yourself up-to-date other products or services useful for backpackers. You can visit our web-site or send us an email through the addresses below :

Internet   **www.Hostels4Backpackers.com**

E-mail   **info@Hostels4Backpackers.com**

Telephone : To & From

When you need to make a call from one country to another country, it's unfortunately not quite as simple as a local call. It's worthwhile reading this whole section - first we'll explain how to make a call from other countries **to** Australia (eg. if you want to make a reservation with a hostel) and how to call **from** Australia to other countries. Then we'll explain how to make calls within Australia.

Here is an example of a typical international call number :

011 - 61 - 2 - 45649923

The first part is the special code you need to dial in order to access international numbers. In the above example the code is 011. This code is just an example, the actual number to dial depends on where you are calling from. For example, whenever you want to dial **from** the U.K. **to** any other country you first need to dial 00. If dialing **from** the U.S.A. to any other country you need to first dial 011. If you want to dial **from** Australia to any other country, you need to first dial 0011. You'll find a list of common international access codes at the end of this section.

The second part of the number is the code for the specific country you want to call. In the above example this is 61, which is the code for Australia. So, for all calls **to** Australia from overseas, you'll use 61 as the second part of the number you dial. If you want to call **from** Australia to another country then you will use that country's specific code, eg. 44 for the U.K. and 1 for the U.S.A. Other common country codes are listed at the end of this section.

The third part of the number is the area code. In Australia, each state usually has it's own area code. In our previous example the area code is 2, which is the code for New South Wales (the state containing the city of Sydney). So, for all calls to Sydney (and the rest of New South Wales) you'll use 2 for the area code. We'll discuss area codes more in a moment.

Finally, the fourth part of the number (45649923 in the example above) is simply the number of the business or person you wish to call. In Australia all regular telephone numbers have 8 digits.

You are probably familiar with area codes between states or regions in your own country. Usually these codes begin with a 0. In fact the area code for Sydney and New South Wales is 02. However, whenever you are calling from one country to another, you should not dial any preceding 0's in the area code. This applies when you are calling to Australia, or when you are calling from Australia to your own country.

When you are dialing within Australia, you **should** include the area code, including the 0, whenever you are dialing a number from a different state. For example, all the telephone numbers in this book are listed first with the area code in brackets, then the hostel's actual number, eg. *(07) 4778-5577.* In this case the area code of 07 is for the state of Queensland. If you are in Queensland then you don't need to dial the area code, however if you are in another state then you will need to dial the full number including the preceding 07. If you are calling from overseas then you would leave out the 0.

Many hostels provide a 1800 number in addition to their normal number. Calling a 1800 number is free, so you don't need to put any coins in the phone and you can talk as long as you like. However, 1800 numbers are not free if you call them from a mobile phone. Also, calling a 1800 number is only free when you are calling from *within* Australia – if you try calling a 1800 number from overseas it may not work, or you may be connected but you will be paying the usual international cost. Although you don't pay for 1800 calls, the hostel is actually paying for the call instead (someone has to pay!) so 1800 calls should only be used for making bookings - not for calling your friends who may be staying at the hostel!

A few of the hostel's 1800 numbers only work when you are calling from *within the same state* as the hostel is located (eg. you and the hostel are both in Queensland), but that is not common. Numbers beginning with 1300 are not free, however these numbers allow you to only pay for a local call (40 cents) even if you're on the other side of Australia – then you can talk as long you like without any extra cost.

Telstra is the name of the company which operates the phone network in Australia. For calls within Australia, the Telstra public telephones usually take either coins or more conveniently the Telstra pre-paid phonecards which you can purchase from newsagents. Calls within the local area cost 40 cents with no time limit. There are also some non-Telstra phones which don't take the usual phonecards and commonly require 50 cents for local calls. The cost to call outside your local area varies according to the distance, so it's best to have a lot of change or a Telstra phonecard.

For calls outside Australia, it's best to use international phonecards which are readily available from a range of companies (not Telstra) and offer incredibly cheap rates to most countries. Brochures with all the latest international phonecard information and rates are usually available at newsagents.

Important Numbers

Police Emergency	000	Phone Directory	12455
Police non-urgent	131-444	Operator Assistance	1234
Fire Emergency	000	Overseas Operator	1225
Ambulance	000	Translation Service	131-450
Medical Care	1300-369-359	Time	1194
Crisis/Counseling	131-114	Weather	1196
Tax Office	132-861	Visa	1800-450-346
American Express	1300-132-639	Mastercard	1800-120-113

Also see the Consulates section for other numbers.

International Codes

As explained in the previous section, when calling from one country to another, you will first need to know the international access number **from** the country you are in, as well as the country code for the country you are calling **to**. Here are some of the more common numbers you'll need :

International Access Numbers

Australia	0011	U.S.A.	011	U.K.	00
Canada	011	Japan	0041	Netherlands	00
Germany	00	France	00	New Zealand	00
Sweden	00	Denmark	00	Switzerland	00

Country Codes

Australia	61	U.S.A.	1	U.K.	44
Canada	1	Japan	81	Netherlands	31
Germany	49	France	33	New Zealand	64
Sweden	46	Denmark	45	Switzerland	41

Prohibited Items

Australia wishes to keeps it's farms and agricultural system free of any possible contamination from overseas insects and other possible problems. So there are strict laws about what can and can't be brought into Australia. You will be given information about this on the plane before you arrive, and there is a bin before the checkpoint so you can dispose of any prohibited items. As a general guide, you should try to avoid bringing any type of food (fresh or packaged), as well as most plant and animal products. Illegal drugs are strictly prohibited and thorough airport security checks are very common, with offenders facing major fines or imprisonment.

You may need to pay tax on some items if you bring them more than these quantities : over 1125ml of alcohol, over 250 cigarettes or 250grams of tobacco, and relatively new items (such as electronics) with a **combined** value over AU$400 - this doesn't apply to items owned and used for at least 12 months. The new items tax is to prevent people bringing items into Australia from overseas specifically to avoid the government importation tax. In most cases this tax isn't requested unless the items are obviously brand new, for example if you've owned a camera for 6 months and it's obviously not new then you probably won't have any problem, but if in doubt bring receipts and documentation to prove length of ownership. Quantities of prescription medicines should be accompanied by a letter from your doctor.

Money

The exchange rate between Australian dollars (AU$) and other currencies changes up and down daily, but as a rough guide, if you come from the USA or Europe you can expect your money to double when you convert it to Australian dollars, and it will triple if you come from the UK. Of course that's only for approximate calculations, don't rely on it! Traveler's checks and cash from overseas can be easily exchanged at banks, airports, and money-changing offices in major cities and popular backpacker destinations. They will all have varying rates and often require fees or commissions, so shop around for the best deal.

You can open a bank account by taking the appropriate identification with you (as much as possible), this allows you to safely deposit your money. You can then withdraw your money from any ATM (automatic money-machine). Or you can pay by simply using your ATM card in many shops (check if they accept 'EFTPOS'). Credit cards are also accepted in most shops, although it's always best to check first, especially in smaller shops (and hostels). Visa and Mastercard are both commonly accepted, with American Express a little less popular but still quite common.

The four biggest banks are ANZ, Commonwealth, National and Westpac. All four have branches across the country and so will allow easy access to your funds. ANZ staff tend to be friendlier and often don't require any paperwork for deposits and withdrawals within the bank.

ATMs and banks also allow you to withdraw money straight from your credit card account back home. Usually you'll be charged a commission fee by the ATM or bank. ATMs often won't inform you of the fees, and even less obvious is that your bank back home may also take it's own separate 'service fee' later, which may be a percentage of the amount you withdraw (sometimes 3% to 10%), or a flat fee such as US$4, depending on your bank. Check with your bank for their international fees, but don't expect to get the correct answer since it seems international services often fall outside the usual experience of bank information staff.

It is also often possible to withdraw money from your regular bank savings account back home, using your bank's standard ATM card (i.e. not credit card). This is theoretically possible if your card displays the logo of one of the international networks such as Cirrus or Maestro, **however** all these card networks are notorious for **very often** not working overseas, so you definitely shouldn't rely on regular ATM cards for your supply of travel cash once you get here. It may also be worthwhile asking your bank if you will need a new PIN number, or even a new card issued, so that it works in Australia – but again, don't rely on your bank's staff to provide accurate information because often your card won't work despite the full assurance that they offer to the contrary. On the other hand, withdrawing money from your credit card account is much more reliable, and on the rare occasions that an

ATM won't accept a credit card then a quick visit inside the bank should allow you to withdraw cash from the inquiries counter (that's also useful if you have a credit card with no PIN number).

Banks are generally open 9.30am to 4pm, Monday to Thursday, and 9.30 to 5pm on Fridays. A few banks may be open on Saturday mornings (look for a chain of banks named St.George). Money changing offices are frequently open Saturdays and Sundays, especially in major tourist areas.

Leaving tips at restaurants and for other services has not been a part of the traditional system in Australia. Tipping has slowly become more common, especially with so many tourists who are used to doing this back home. You will still almost never be expected to leave a tip, but of course if the service is particularly good and you want to leave a tip then the staff will certainly appreciate your generosity.

Time Differences

There are 3 different time zones in Australia :

Eastern Standard Time (EST) is used in the states of New South Wales (NSW), Queensland (QLD), Victoria (VIC), Tasmania (TAS), and the Australian Capital Territory (ACT).

Central Standard Time is 30 minutes behind EST and is used in the states of South Australia (SA) and the Northern Territory (NT).

Western Standard Time is 2 hours behind EST and is only used in the state of Western Australia (WA).

During the months from October to March there is 'Daylight Savings', which means that the time changes in some states. In October, the state of South Australia and all states using EST change their clocks forward one hour, except Queensland which stays the same. In March those states all change their clocks back an hour.

Australian EST is 10+ hours from GMT (Greenwich Mean Time, the standard for international time conversion). The chart below shows some examples for helping to calculate the difference between Australian EST time and some major cities. However, the chart does **not** take into account 'Daylight Savings', which affects most time zones in Australia from October to March, and this may also affect the times of other countries during the opposite months (eg. the U.K. and U.S.A. from around April to October), so it's very likely that your calculations will need to take that into account.

Time Zone

		Example : When it's 8pm
		in Sydney, it's…
Sydney	GMT+10	
Tokyo	GMT+9	7pm in Tokyo
Los Angeles	GMT-8	2am in Los Angeles
New York	GMT-5	5am in New York
London	GMT+0	10am in London
Berlin	GMT+1	11am in Berlin

Travel within Australia

Buses/Coaches are the most popular way for backpackers to get around Australia. Greyhound, McCafferty's and Pioneer are all major bus companies covering many routes around Australia, and all offer single destination tickets or a range of monthly multi-stop passes. There are also other companies such as the popular Oz Experience that exclusively provide bus services to backpackers, often traveling along more scenic and interesting routes rather than the most direct, and with the driver-guides offering some commentary and entertainment. Before buying any multi-stop bus pass, read all the 'fine print' carefully to be sure it suits your needs and destinations.

There are also many discount plane fares available, sometimes being similar or even cheaper than the equivalent bus fare (although you won't see so much along the way). In most capitals and popular backpacker towns you'll find a backpacker-specialist travel agency which can help in finding the best airfares. Normal travel agencies can also help, although they're often not so motivated to find the cheapest options available.

Traveling by car or campervan is definitely the most flexible way to see Australia, allowing you to start and stop whenever and wherever you wish, and see every attraction along the way. Most overseas licenses are valid for driving in Australia, so long as they remain valid in your home country. You will need to keep your license with you while driving, and if your license is not printed in English you'll also require an official translation (usually available as some form of 'international driving permit' from your local automobile association). Overseas licenses are valid for driving in Australia for up to 6 months, if you require a longer time then you'll need an international driving permit from your home country, or you can apply for an Australian license once you're here (requiring payment and usually a driving and written test).

There are a range of options if you choose to self-drive in Australia. Many people buy an old second-hand car, either from a private seller advertising in the newspaper, or through a second-hand car dealership. Private sellers usually offer much lower prices, but dealers often provide limited warranties so this can be a safer choice, and they'll also help take care of all the necessary paperwork. If you're driving a long distance then perhaps the cheapest car isn't such a good idea, or you could find yourself in the middle of nowhere with repairs costing more than the initial cost of the car. Newer cars may be more reliable but again may also require unexpected major repairs, especially in the Australian heat – be sure to regularly check your oil and water levels (not when the engine is hot!).

In capital cities and some other popular backpacker regions you'll often find car advertisements from fellow backpackers on the notice-board in your hostel. These are often good value since they are priced to sell quickly and have often proved themselves worthy of long journeys – but you can never know if there's an expensive repair job just around the corner.

Whenever buying a car in Australia, you are legally required to officially transfer the registration to your name. This also partially protects you from buying a lemon, because all transfers require certified safety checks which will note any obvious problems (but there may be many non-obvious problems). Some backpackers buy cars from fellow backpackers without transferring the registration, that is certainly easy but it will make it harder for you to sell the car later, and it will also make it almost impossible for you to renew the registration when it runs out.

Hire cars and campervans are very popular and most include extensive insurance and 24-hour roadside assistance, providing you with peace of mind as you know that all possible setbacks will be taken care of. This can also work out relatively inexpensive when sharing the cost between a few people. Be sure to read all the 'fine print' of the rental agreement thoroughly.

In Australia, seat-belts are required to be worn by the driver and all passengers at all times. It's also illegal to drive and talk on a mobile phone at the same time. All laws are thoroughly enforced, with large fines or license cancellation possible. All driving is on the left side of the road, with the steering wheel on the right side of the car. Be sure to learn all the road rules of Australia before starting your driving. Also be sure to break up longer drives with frequent rest stops – fatigue on long country roads is a major cause of fatal accidents.

Safety & Health

No vaccinations are necessary before entering Australia. The only exception is if you have visited Africa or South America during the previous six days before entering Australia, in which case you'll need a yellow fever vaccination before you arrive.

Australia has a low rate of crime compared to many other countries, and unlike many tourist areas of Europe there are not many pickpockets in Australia. Nevertheless, you should always take standard precautions to protect against any possibility of misfortune. Try to avoid walking in secluded areas after dark, always keep an eye on your luggage, don't openly show how much money you have in your wallet, etc. Also leave photocopies of important documents (eg. your passport information page, credit cards and airline tickets) with friends or relatives back home. And be sure to bring along a padlock to use with the lockers which many hostels provide.

Swimming is part of the Australian way of life, and virtually every Australian has a good swimming ability. Unfortunately this is not the case with tourists, and quite a few drown every year. Even good swimmers may have trouble in unfamiliar conditions, and Australian waves may be considerably larger than back home. If in any doubt then don't go too far in, a good guideline is just deep enough for the water to be up to your waist and no higher.

There are frequently strong underwater currents, known as rips, which can quickly pull swimmers out into the deeper waters of the ocean. If this occurs, **do not swim against the current**. You will need to relax and allow yourself to continue floating in the rip, eventually it will end by itself and you can then swim back to shore. If you try to escape the rip by fighting against it's strong pull, you will almost definitely cause yourself extreme exhaustion and this results in the drowning deaths of tourists every year.

Life guards patrol many of the main beaches around Australia. If life guards are present and watching the beach then there will be red-yellow flags in the sand. The life guards are watching the area **between** the red-yellow flags, and that is the area you should swim in. The flags have been placed in the safest area for you to swim, free of any hidden rips and other dangers. In some areas (such as the Gold Coast) you may only be allowed to swim between the flags, so expect embarrassing loudspeaker announcements asking you to leave the water if you choose to ignore the flags! In areas where there are no life guard patrols, use your common-sense and swim as safely as possible – never alone. If you are having trouble in the water and need to be rescued, you can signal your distress by raising one arm in the air.

Most beaches north of Hervey Bay on the east coast of Queensland have a season of very dangerous jellyfish, with potentially deadly stinger tentacles. This occurs only in the warmer months, especially November to April. Most beaches have signs warning people not to swim when it's 'stinger season', but even if there's no sign you still shouldn't take the risk – it's not uncommon to read a story in the newspaper about yet another tourist ignoring the warnings, and ending up with a very painful and expensive helicopter trip to the nearest hospital. Fortunately, most popular coastal areas have pools or special netted areas at the beach so you can still stay cool and wet in the summer heat. First aid for jellyfish stings is (1) apply vinegar if available - this can help to neutralize the poison, (2) **don't rub any remaining stinger-tentacle off the body** - rubbing releases more poison and will make the situation worse, and (3) seek medical attention immediately.

Sunscreen is also absolutely essential for the safety of your skin. Australia has the highest rate of skin cancer in the world, due to the hole in the ozone. Even on days when it's cloudy or the sun doesn't seem very bright, many travelers may get burned after prolonged exposure since their skin isn't used to Australia's particularly intense rays. Hats are useful, and sunscreen is vital, especially in Summer or any day when you'll be in the sun for some time. Always check the sunscreen's official protection rating, 15+ is the recommended **minimum** and 30+ is generally best, especially for more sensitive skin or exposure during the middle of the day.

The hot weather also brings the possibility of dehydration and heat exhaustion, so be sure to drink plenty of water and avoid strenuous activities out in the mid-day sun. If the extreme heat really upsets you then avoid the northern states and inland areas in Summer and stay in more southerly coastal regions. Some southerly areas can still be quite hot in Summer but it's not so extreme.

Travelers from some countries are entitled to free immediate healthcare according to international agreements. These countries include the U.K., New Zealand, Sweden, Italy, the Netherlands, Malta and Finland. You may need to show evidence of being enrolled in your own country's health care system, and some limitations to treatment or duration of stay may apply. For more information and to register you will need to call Medicare (the Australian public health organization) on 132-011 or send an email to *medicare.enq@hic.gov.au*

Visas

Everyone entering Australia requires a visa **before** arriving in Australia (the only exception is visitors from New Zealand who receive their visa upon arrival). Tourist visas are usually issued for 3 months, with 6 months sometimes being an option. If you wish to work while traveling, or you wish to stay in Australia for up to a year, you'll need a 'working holiday visa' – see the work section of this book for more details. When booking your flight to Australia, your travel agent will usually provide you with the necessary paperwork for obtaining visas, or will point you in the right direction for contacting your nearest Australian consulate or embassy.

Travelers from some countries are eligible to receive an 'Electronic Travel Authority' (ETA). This is like a pre-approval for a visa. First you obtain your approved ETA, which unlike a regular visa does not require you to send your passport away for any stamps or labels. Then when you get to Australia your ETA entitles you to receive the standard visa in your passport. This is obviously faster and more convenient than a regular visa, however ETAs can only be used for 3 month visas, and ETAs are only available to visitors from some countries. Your travel agent or local Australian embassy can provide you with more information about this.

Upon entering Australia you will need to have a passport which is valid for at least six months longer than you are planning on staying, even if you're only staying a few days or weeks.

Finding a Job

In order to work legally in Australia you will need to obtain a 'working holiday visa' (not the standard 'tourist visa) **before** arriving here. Not everyone is eligible for working holiday visas, mostly depending on your age and nationality (contact your local Australian embassy or consulate for details). If you are eligible, your working holiday visa will usually allow you to stay for 12 months.

Upon arrival you will also need to obtain an Australian bank account (take as much personal identification with you as possible), and an Australian 'tax file number' (visit the city's local tax office or call their information line). Tax is usually automatically taken from your wages, so expect to only see about 70% after tax has been deducted. It's possible to make a little or a lot, depending on the hours and type of work you find, and it's also a great way to meet the locals and support your further travels at the same time. You can work for as many companies as you wish during your stay, but there is a maximum limit of 3 months with a single employer.

In most capital cities it's fairly easy to find work in restaurants, offices and factories. City and suburban local newspapers may have vacancies, but for finding a job quickly it's often best to join a recruitment agency who will then help to find you something suitable. You can find employment/recruitment agencies in the 'Yellow Pages' phone directory, or ask for help at your hostel. It's also usually best to bring a resume/C.V. with you (you can also usually type a new one with your current details in most internet cafes or libraries), and don't forget appropriate clothes. Many hostels have notice boards with job vacancies from local companies. There may also be jobs available in the hostel, offering free accommodation and/or cash in exchange for a few hours work.

Harvest work usually involves picking and packing fruit and vegetables. This type of work is very common for backpackers and is easy to find, but it is rarely easy work - many people quit after complaining that it's back-breaking labor, often from very early in the morning into the mid-day heat, and the pay is often not great. Despite that, some people do enjoy it and continue for a month or two, making many new friends while saving for the next leg of the journey. Harvest work is available in many different areas around the country, for example in Queensland near Cairns and Mission Beach, and in the Victorian towns of Mildura and Echuca. Since it can take quite a long time to get to some country regions, always check that work is available **before** traveling there! A good source of information regarding current harvest work is the government agency Employment National. They have a 'Harvest Hotline' which can be called on 1300-720-126, or visit their web-site at *www.employmentnational.com.au*

Mail

Post offices are generally open from 9am to 5pm, Monday to Friday. Some major post offices may open on Saturday mornings. Stamps are also commonly available at newsagents. You can have mail or packages from overseas sent to you care of most post offices in Australia by having them marked with (1) the words 'Poste Restante' (2) your name (3) the post office location (City / State / Australia). Be sure to have official identification with you when picking up your mail. You can also usually have mail sent to hostels where you're staying.

International Consulates

Here is a list of contact numbers for the Australian government embassies or consulates in some of the more common countries. You may wish to contact these local Australian consulates regarding visa requirements or other general inquiries, although your travel agent will usually provide this information to you when you book your airline ticket.

U.S.A.	(202) 797-3000	U.K.	(020) 7379-4334
Canada	(613) 236-0841	Japan	(03) 5232-4111
Netherlands	(070) 310-8200	Germany	(030) 880-0880
New Zealand	(09) 921-8800	France	(01) 4059-3300
Switzerland	(22) 799-9100	Sweden	(08) 613-2900

You probably won't need to contact your country's local embassy in Australia unless you lose your passport or something else major happens. Here are the numbers for some of the most common embassies in Australia :

U.S.A	(02) 9373-9200	U.K.	(03) 9650-3699
Canada	(02) 9364-3000	Japan	(02) 9231-3455
Netherlands	(02) 9387-6644	Germany	(02) 9328-7733
New Zealand	(02) 9247-1999	France	(02) 9261-5779
Switzerland	(02) 9369-4244	Sweden	(02) 9262-6433

Other Information

Electricity in Australia is supplied at 240volts, and 220volt appliances usually work fine also. If your electrical devices use 220/240volts but have a different plug-end, adapters are available very cheaply from electronic stores. However if your electrical device uses 110/120 volts then you will also ***NEED*** a voltage adapter which is more expensive and not so readily available.

The legal age for drinking alcohol and entry to nightclubs is 18. Be sure to carry proof of age with you.

The official language of Australia is English – not 'Australian' as some tourists believe before arrival! Despite that, the locals may have strong accents with plenty of 'Ozzie' slang, and this can make it seem almost like another language which other English-speaking people may not understand at first! Don't worry, in time your brain will adapt to the change and you may leave the country speaking with an Australian accent!

Measurement in Australia uses the metric system, following is a chart showing how to convert to and from the old imperial system :

miles = kilometers (km) x 0.62
kilometers = miles x 1.6
pounds = kilograms (kg) x 2.2046
kilograms = pounds x 0.4536 kg
Fahrenheit = degrees Celsius x 1.8 + 32
Celsius = degrees Fahrenheit -32 x 0.55555

Corrections / Disclaimer

Although we have taken all reasonable care to ensure that the information in this book is correct and accurate, we do advise that information is liable to change, so the details here are to be used as a guide only. We welcome any corrections and updates for future editions of the book, please send the information through our web-site or email address below :

Internet   **www.Hostels4Backpackers.com**

E-mail   **info@Hostels4Backpackers.com**

Please note that information provided about hostels and any other third party in this book does not indicate in any way that the book's publishers and authors endorse or recommend any of these hostels or third parties. The book publishers and authors are not liable in any way for any inconvenience caused, or expense incurred by the use of the information provided within this book, including as a result of any inaccurate or incorrect information. Under no circumstances will the publishers or authors accept any responsibility or liability for any damages (incidental, consequential, direct or indirect). In other words, you are responsible for your own travels! We wish you happy journeying with the least amount of hassle!

Map / Distances

Darwin

NORTHERN
TERRITORY

Broome

WESTERN
AUSTRALIA

Alice Springs

Ningaloo
Reef

Monkey
Mia

SOUTH
AUSTRALIA

Perth

Adelaide

Cairns
350	**Townsville**												
650	300	**Airlie Beach**											
1600	1250	950	**Hervey Bay**										
1900	1550	1300	350	**Brisbane**									
2100	1750	1450	550	200	**Byron Bay**								
2350	2000	1700	750	400	250	**Coffs Harbour**							
2900	2550	2300	1350	1000	800	600	**Sydney**						
3200	2850	2550	1600	1250	1100	850	300	**Canberra**					
3350	3200	2700	2000	1650	1700	1450	850	600	**Melbourne**				
3900	3750	3250	2500	2200	2300	2050	1500	1250	750	**Adelaide**			
2950	2550	2850	3800	3600	3750	4000	4500	4350	3800	3100	**Darwin**		
2400	2050	2350	3300	3050	3250	3600	3000	2800	2300	1550	1500	**Alice Springs**	
4050	3850	4150	5100	5450	5600	5900	6000	6250	6050	5250	2650	2850	**Broome**
6650	6600	6850	7750	8150	5350	4400	4500	4050	3550	2800	4450	3700	2500	**Perth**

Connect any 2 cities in the chart below
to find the approximate distance

28

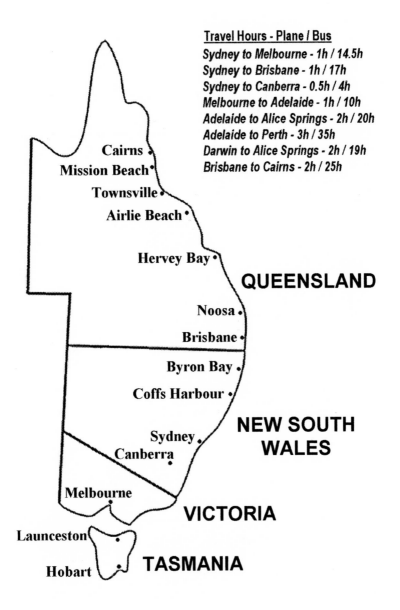

Travel Hours - Plane / Bus
Sydney to Melbourne - 1h / 14.5h
Sydney to Brisbane - 1h / 17h
Sydney to Canberra - 0.5h / 4h
Melbourne to Adelaide - 1h / 10h
Adelaide to Alice Springs - 2h / 20h
Adelaide to Perth - 3h / 35h
Darwin to Alice Springs - 2h / 19h
Brisbane to Cairns - 2h / 25h

Cairns
Mission Beach
Townsville
Airlie Beach

Hervey Bay

QUEENSLAND

Noosa
Brisbane
Byron Bay
Coffs Harbour

NEW SOUTH
WALES

Sydney
Canberra

Melbourne

VICTORIA

Launceston

Hobart

TASMANIA

New South Wales (NSW)

New South Wales has something to offer everyone. Starting in Sydney, there's the obvious attractions of the Opera House and Harbour Bridge, and the famous Bondi and Manly beaches. Of course that's just the start, with shopping and entertainment at Darling Harbour, a variety of activities, markets, and endless nightlife, it's no surprise that many travelers spend a long time here before beginning the journey north, south or west.

The spectacular Blue Mountains are only a short trip west from Sydney and offer bushwalking, waterfalls and caves. Inland west has a variety of opportunities to experience real working Australian farms and other country activities such as horse-riding, and there's great snow skiing in the mountains in season. Also inland is Canberra, Australia's national capital.

Heading south from Sydney, along the coast towards Victoria, are many interesting smaller towns, as well as over 100 beaches offering surfing and other activities, National Parks and more.

Heading north from Sydney along the central coast you'll come to popular backpacker destinations like Newcastle, Port Stephens and Coffs Harbour. Further up on the north coast are even more beaches, sun and fun, and no trip to Australia would be complete without staying a while in Byron Bay, home of alternative culture. And then you're just a short distance from reaching Queensland, the 'Sunshine State'...

Sydney - City Central

For the majority of backpackers, Sydney is where it all begins, and it's certainly a great place to start exploring everything that Australia has to offer

One of the most well-known landmarks in Sydney is the Harbour Bridge - you can climb the South-East tower for just a few dollars and the view is amazing, or take a guided tour all the way to the very top of the bridge if you have a budget to match! Nearby is an area known as 'the Rocks', the site of Sydney's first European settlement, much of which is still preserved from colonial times.

The Opera House is another famous landmark worth a visit. Nearby, Circular Quay is the launching point for many sight-seeing cruises, as well as cheaper regular ferry services which can sometimes offer the same great sights (try the ferry to Manly). Also nearby are the beautifully-presented Royal Botanic Gardens, definitely worth a visit.

Then there's the Art Gallery, Taronga Zoo, the Sky Tower, Chinatown & Paddy's Market, Darling Harbour, and an endless variety of nightclubs, pubs and social 'buzz'..

Indy's Planet Backpack Sydney

198 Elizabeth St
Sydney NSW 2000

Phone   (02) 9211-4200
Fax   (02) 9211-7530
Freecall 1800-774-545
E-mail   *goindys@indysbackpackers.com.au*
Internet *www.indysbackpackers.com.au*

Wood Duck Inn

Hotel William, 49 William St
East Sydney NSW 2010

Phone   (02) 9358-5856
Freecall 1800-110-025
E-mail   *duck@woodduckinn.com.au*
Internet *www.woodduckinn.com.au*

Wanderers on Kent

477 Kent St
Sydney NSW 2000

Phone   (02) 9267-7718
Freecall 1800-424-444
E-mail   *info@wanderersonkent.com.au*
Internet *www.wanderersonkent.com.au*

City Central Backpackers

752 George St
Sydney NSW 2000

Phone   (02) 9212-4833
Fax   (02) 9212-5753
Freecall 1800-249-910
E-mail *enquiry@ccbackpack.com.au*
Internet *www.ccbackpack.com.au*

Downtown City Backpackers

611 George St
Sydney NSW 2000

Phone   (02) 9211-8801
Fax   (02) 9211-8803
Freecall 1800-248-815
E-mail *enquiry@downtowncity.com.au*
Internet *www.downtowncity.com.au*

Footprints Westend

412 Pitt St
Sydney NSW 2000

Phone   (02) 9211-4588
Fax   (02) 9211-5312
Freecall 1800-013-186
E-mail *info@footprintswestend.com.au*
Internet *www.footprintswestend.com.au*

The George Street Private Hotel

700a George St
Sydney NSW 2000

Phone (02) 9211-1800
Fax (02) 9211-1800
Freecall 1800-679-606
E-mail *bookings@georgehotel.com.au*
Internet *www.georgehotel.com.au*

Hyde Park Backpackers

88-90 Wentworth Avenue
Sydney NSW 2000

Phone (02) 9282-9266
E-mail *hydepark.stay@bigpond.com*
Internet *www.hydeparkbackpackers.com.au*

Maze Backpackers

417 Pitt St
Sydney NSW 2000

Phone (02) 9211-5115
Fax (02) 9281-9605
Freecall 1800-813-522
E-mail *contact@mazebackpackers.com*
Internet *www.mazebackpackers.com*

Sydney Backpackers

Victoria House, 7 Wilmot St
Sydney NSW 2000

Phone   (02) 9267-7772
Fax   (02) 9267-2272
Freecall 1800-887-766
E-mail   *info@sydneybackpackers.com*
Internet *www.sydneybackpackers.com*

Wake Up!

509 Pitt St
Sydney NSW 2000

Phone   (02) 9288-7888
Fax   (02) 9288-7889
E-mail   *info@wakeup.com.au*
Internet *www.wakeup.com.au*

Sydney Central YHA

11 Rawson Place
Sydney NSW 2000

Phone   (02) 9281-9111
Fax   (02) 9281-9199
E-mail   *sydcentral@yhansw.org.au*
Internet *www.yha.org.au*

BIG

212 Elizabeth St
Surry Hills NSW 2010

Phone   (02) 9281-6030
Fax   (02) 9281-6031
Freecall 1800-284-639
E-mail   *bookings@bigonelizabeth.com*
Internet *www.bigonelizabeth.com*

Kangaroo Backpack

665 South Dowling St
Surry Hills NSW 2010

Phone   (02) 9319-5915
Fax   (02) 9318-0902
E-mail   *reservations@kangaroobakpak.com.au*
Internet *www.kangaroobakpak.com.au*

Australian Backpackers

132 Bourke St
Woolloomooloo NSW 2011

Phone   (02) 9331-0822
Fax   (02) 9331-0966
Freecall 1800-350-211
E-mail   *ausbak@hotmail.com*
Internet *www.australianbackpackers.com.au*

Sydney - Kings Cross

Kings Cross is one of the major backpacker hotspots in Sydney. Only a short walk from the city center, 'the Cross' is home to a variety of pubs, nightclubs and non-stop parties. It's also Sydney's main 'red light district', so prostitutes and strip-clubs are not an unusual sight. Some of the more sensitive travelers may find this disturbing, but the vast majority of travelers, including single women, do feel safe at all times. For most travelers, Kings Cross is an fun place to visit with an exciting vibe, 24 hours a day...

Backpackers Headquarters Hostel

79 Bayswater Rd
Kings Cross NSW 2011

Phone   (02) 9331-6180
Fax   (02) 9331-6180
E-mail   *headquartershostel@mail.com*
Internet *www.backpackershqhostel.com.au*

Boomerang Backpackers

141 William St
Kings Cross NSW 2011

Phone   (02) 8354-0488
Fax   (02) 8356-9067
Freecall 1800-266-636
E-mail   *info@boomerangbackpackers.com*
Internet *www.boomerangbackpackers.com*

Cooee Travellers Accommodation

107-109 Darlinghurst Rd
Kings Cross NSW 2011

Phone   (02) 9331-0009
Fax   (02) 9331-1781
Freecall 1800-200-793
E-mail   *info@cooeetravellers.com*
Internet *www.cooeetravellers.com*

Crossroad Backpackers

174 Victoria St
Kings Cross NSW 2011

Phone   (02) 9356-4551
Fax   (02) 9356-4551
E-mail   *jenny0502@hotmail.com*
Internet *www.crossroadbackpackers.com*

Funk House Backpackers

23 Darlinghurst Rd
Kings Cross NSW 2011

Phone   (02) 9358-6455
Fax   (02) 9358-3506
Freecall 1800-247-600
E-mail   *goodtimes@funkhouse.com.au*
Internet *www.funkhouse.com.au*

Jolly Swagman Backpackers

27 Orwell St
Kings Cross NSW 2011

Phone   (02) 9358-6400
Fax   (02) 9357-4733
Freecall 1800-805-870
E-mail   *stay@jollyswagman.com.au*
Internet *www.jollyswagman.com.au*

Lido Bak Pak Apartments

2 Roslyn St
Kings Cross NSW 2011

Phone   (02) 9358-4844
Fax   (02) 9380-2690
E-mail   *Lido@lidobackpack.com*
Internet *www.lidobackpack.com*

The Original Backpackers Lodge

160-162 Victoria St
Kings Cross NSW 2011

Phone   (02) 9356-3232
Fax   (02) 9368-1435
Freecall 1800-807-130
E-mail   *info@originalbackpackers.com.au*
Internet *www.originalbackpackers.com.au*

Pink House

6-8 Barncleuth Square
Kings Cross NSW 2011

Phone   (02) 9358-1689
Fax   (02) 9358-1689
Freecall 1800-806-384
E-mail   *info@pinkhouse.com.au*
Internet *www.pinkhouse.com.au*

The Globe Backpackers

40 Darlinghurst Rd
Kings Cross NSW 2011

Phone   (02) 9326-9675
Freecall 1800-806-384
E-mail   *theglobe@qd.com.au*
Internet *www.qd.com.au/~theglobe*

Sydney Central Backpackers

16 Orwell St
Kings Cross NSW 2011

Phone   (02) 9358-6600
Fax   (02) 9356-3799
Freecall 1800-440-202
E-mail   *info@sydneybackpackers.com.au*
Internet *www.sydneybackpackers.com.au*

Kanga House

141 Victoria St
Kings Cross NSW 2011

Phone   (02) 9357-7897
Fax   (02) 8354-0439
Freecall 1800-4-KANGA
E-mail   *info@kangahouse.com.au*
Internet *www.kangahouse.com.au*

V Backpackers

144 Victoria St
Kings Cross NSW 2011

Phone   (02) 9357-4733
Freecall 1800-667-225
E-mail   *stay@vbackpackers.com*
Internet *www.vbackpackers.com*

Eva's Backpackers

6 Orwell St
Kings Cross NSW 2011

Phone   (02) 9358-2185
Fax   (02) 9358-3259
E-mail   *info@evasbackpackers.com.au*
Internet *www.evasbackpackers.com.au*

Bernly Private Hotel

15 Springfield Avenue
Potts Point NSW 2011

Phone   (02) 9358-3122
Fax   (02) 9356-4405
E-mail   *bernly@bernlyprivatehotel.com.au*
Internet *www.bernlyprivatehotel.com.au*

Blue Parrot Backpackers

87 Macleay St
Potts Point NSW 2011

Phone   (02) 9356-4888
Fax   (02) 9356-4898
Freecall 1800-252-299
E-mail   *bparrot@bigpond.net.au*
Internet *www.blueparrot.com.au*

Montpelier Hotel

39a Elizabeth Bay Rd
Elizabeth Bay NSW 2011

Phone   (02) 9358-6960
Fax   (02) 9380-9466
E-mail   *montpelier@pacific.net.au*

Sydney - Beaches

Sydney's beaches are great for getting into the Australian sun. The surfing is great, boards are available for hire and lessons are available for beginners, so you have no excuses! Beach areas also tend to have plenty of nightlife and partying nearby (it goes with the life-style!)

Bondi is the most famous beach and is quite close to the city. The suburb name is pronounced like 'bond-eye'. Bondi has a deservedly great reputation, however it's popularity means that when the weather is best, you could be sharing the sand with more people than you had in mind. Manly is a great beach that comes a close second in reputation and popularity, and is further from the city center so it's generally less crowded. There are also plenty of other beaches around Sydney to explore...

Biltmore on Bondi

110 Campbell Parade
Bondi NSW 2026

Phone   (02) 9130-4660
Fax   (02) 9365-0195
Freecall 1800-304-660
E-mail   *biltmorehotel@hotmail.com*

Noah's Bondi Beach

2 Campbell Parade
Bondi NSW 2026

Phone   (02) 9365-7100
Freecall 1800-226-662
E-mail   *noahsbondibeach@aol.com*
Internet *www.noahsbondibeach.com*

Lamrock Lodge

19 Lamrock Avenue
Bondi NSW 2026

Phone   (02) 9130-5063
Freecall 1800-625-063
E-mail   *admin@lamrocklodge.com*
Internet *www.lamrocklodge.com*

Bondi Beachouse YHA

Corner Fletcher & Dellview Sts
Bondi NSW 2026

Phone   (02) 9365-2088
Fax   (02) 9365-2177
E-mail   *bondi@intercoast.com.au*
Internet *www.bondibeachouse.com.au*

Bondi Sands Hotel

252 Campbell Parade
Bondi NSW 2026

Phone   (02) 9365-3703
Fax   (02) 9365-5822
Freecall 1800-026-634
E-mail   *bookings@bondisands.com*
Internet *www.bondisands.com*

Lochner's Guesthouse

27 Paul St
Bondi Junction NSW 2022

Phone   (02) 9387-2162
Fax   (02) 9389-7247
E-mail   *info@lochnersguesthouse.com.au*
Internet *www.lochnersguesthouse.com.au*

Manly Bunkhouse

35 Pine St
Manly NSW 2095

Phone   (02) 9976-0472
Fax   (02) 9977-0692
Freecall 1800-657-122
E-mail   *sales@bunkhouse.com.au*
Internet *www.bunkhouse.com.au*

Manly Backpackers Beachside

28 Raglan St
Manly NSW 2095

Phone   (02) 9977-3411
Fax   (02) 9977-4379
Freecall 1800-656-299
E-mail   *inquirymanlybackpackers@bigpond.com*
Internet *www.manlybackpackers.com.au*

Manly Beach Hut

7 Pine St
Manly NSW 2095

Phone   (02) 9977-8777
Fax   (02) 9977-8766
Freecall 1800-446-622
E-mail   *enquiry@manlybeachhut.com.au*
Internet *www.manlybeachhut.com.au*

Manly Cove Guest House

51 Wood St
Manly NSW 2095

Phone   (02) 9977-0759
E-mail   *info@manlycvguesthouse.com.au*
Internet *www.manlycvguesthouse.com.au*

Manly Cottage Inn

25 Pittwater Rd
Manly NSW 2095

Phone   (02) 9976-0297
Fax   (02) 9944-0621
E-mail   *ManlyCottage@bigpond.com*
Internet *www.users.bigpond.com/manlycottage*

Wharf Backpackers

48 East Esplanade
Manly NSW 2095

Phone   (02) 9977-2800
Fax   (02) 9977-2820
E-mail   *wharfbackpackers@hotmail.com*

The Steyne Hotel

75 The Corso
Manly NSW 2095

Phone   (02) 9977-4977
Fax   (02) 9977-5645
E-mail   *stay@steynehotel.com.au*
Internet *www.steynehotel.com.au*

The Aegean Lodge

40 Coogee Bay Rd
Coogee NSW 2031

Phone   (02) 9314-5324
Fax   (02) 9398-4055
E-mail   *email@aegeancoogee.com.au*
Internet *www.aegeancoogee.com.au*

Surfside Backpackers

186 Arden St
Coogee NSW 2034

Phone   (02) 9315-7888
Fax   (02) 9315-7892
Freecall 1800-807-872
E-mail   *info@surfsidebackpackers.com.au*
Internet *www.surfsidebackpackers.com.au*

Wizard of Oz Backpackers

172 & 178 Coogee Bay Rd
Coogee NSW 2034

Phone   (02) 9315-7876
Fax   (02) 9315-8974
Freecall 1800-013-460
E-mail   *info@wizardofoz.com.au*
Internet *www.wizardofoz.com.au*

Castle Backpackers

272 Clovelly Rd
Clovelly Beach NSW 2031

Phone   (02) 9665-1824
Fax   (02) 9665-3673
Freecall 1800-857-004
E-mail   *info@castlebackpackers.com*
Internet *www.castlebackpackers.com*

Sydney Beachouse YHA

4 Collaroy St
Collaroy Beach NSW 2026

Phone   (02) 9981-1177
Fax   (02) 9981-1114
E-mail   *mail@sydneybeachouse.com.au*
Internet *www.sydneybeachouse.com.au*

Cronulla Beach YHA

40-42 Kingsway
Cronulla NSW 2229

Phone   (02) 9527-7772
Fax   (02) 9527-0533
E-mail   *enquiries@cronullabeachyha.com*
Internet *www.cronullabeachyha.com*

Sydney - Suburbs

Sydney's suburbs have a lot to offer, especially for travelers looking for a more laid-back atmosphere (although the partying is always close when you want it). Suburbs such as Glebe, Newtown, and Paddington are all only a short distance from the city and are very popular, all with their own special attractions, such as groovy 2nd-hand clothes shops, markets, etc. By staying outside the city you are also more likely to get a feeling for Sydney as experienced by the locals, not just the inner-city 'buzz'.

The Lodge Annandale

96-98 Johnston St
Annandale NSW 2038

Phone   (02) 9660-4600
Fax   (02) 9660-4584
E-mail *info@sydneycity.com.au*
Internet *www.sydneycity.com.au/backpack.html*

Balmain Backpackers

675 Darling St
Balmain NSW 2039

Phone   (02) 9555-6436
Fax   (02) 9555-6051
Freecall 1800-888-640
E-mail *balmainbackpackers@yahoo.com.au*
Internet *www.backpackersydney.com*

Noah Lodge

179 Cleveland St
Chippendale NSW 2008

Phone (02) 8303-1303
Fax (02) 8303-1300
Freecall 1800-300-882
E-mail *bookings@noahlodge.com.au*
Internet *www.noahlodge.com.au*

Dulwich Hill YHA

407 Marrickville Rd
Dulwich Hill NSW 2203

Phone (02) 9550-0054
Fax (02) 9550-0570
E-mail *dulwichhillyha@oranalodge.com.au*
Internet *www.yha.org.au*

Forest Lodge Hotel

117 Arundel St
Glebe NSW 2037

Phone (02) 9660-1872
Fax (02) 9552-1053
Freecall 1800-688-815
E-mail *info@forestlodgehotel.com.au*
Internet *www.forestlodgehotel.com.au*

Alishan International Guest House

100 Glebe Point Rd
Glebe NSW 2037

Phone   (02) 9566-4048
Fax   (02) 9525-4686
E-mail *kevin@alishan.com.au*
Internet *www.alishan.com.au*

Wattle House

44 Hereford St
Glebe NSW 2037

Phone   (02) 9552-4997
Fax   (02) 9660-2528
E-mail *stay@wattlehouse.com.au*
Internet *www.wattlehouse.com.au*

Glebe Point YHA

262-264 Glebe Point Rd
Glebe NSW 2037

Phone   (02) 9692-8418
Fax   (02) 9660-0431
E-mail *glebe@yhansw.org.au*
Internet *www.yha.org.au*

Glebe Village Backpackers

256 Glebe Point Rd
Glebe NSW 2037

Phone   (02) 9660-8133
Fax   (02) 9571-9048
Freecall 1800-801-983
E-mail   *infoglebe@bakpakgroup.com*
Internet *www.bakpakgroup.com/glebevillage*

Glenferrie Lodge

12a Carabella St
Kirribilli NSW 2061

Phone   (02) 9955-1685
Fax   (02) 9929-9439
Freecall 1800-121-011
E-mail   *mail@glenferrielodge.com*
Internet *www.glenferrielodge.com*

Ku-ring-gai National Park Lodge YHA

via Halls Wharf
Morning Bay via Church Point NSW 2105

Phone   (02) 9999-5748
Fax   (02) 9999-5749
E-mail   *pittwater@yhansw.org.au*
Internet *www.yha.org.au*

Billabong Gardens

5-11 Egan St
Newtown NSW 2042

Phone   (02) 9550-3236
Fax   (02) 9550-4352
Freecall 1800-806-419
E-mail   *book@billabonggardens.com.au*
Internet *www.billabonggardens.com.au*

Cooper's Arms Hotel

221 King St
Newtown NSW 2042

Phone   (02) 9550-3461
E-mail   *coopers@zip.com.au*
Internet *www.coopersarms.com.au*

Abbey on King

379 King St
Newtown NSW 2042

Phone   (02) 9519-2099
Fax   (02) 9519-1299
Freecall 1800-219-999
E-mail   *info@theabbeyonking.com.au*
Internet *www.theabbeyonking.com.au*

Captain Cook Hotel

162 Flinders St
Paddington NSW 2021

Phone   (02) 9360-4327
Fax   (02) 9331-8289
Freecall 1800-666-237
E-mail   *captaincookhotel@yahoo.com.au*
Internet *www.captaincookhotel.com.au*

Olympic Hotel

308 Moore Park Rd
Paddington NSW 2021
Phone   (02) 9361-6315
Fax   (02) 9331-5396
E-mail   *olympichotel@bigpond.com*
Internet *www.olympichotel.com.au*

Explorers Lodge

111 Station St
Penrith NSW 2750
Phone   (02) 4731-3616
Fax   (02) 4731-3191
E-mail   *redback@pnc.com.au*
Internet *www.explorerslodge.com*

Kriskindl Guesthouse

22a Hillcrest St
Tempe NSW 2044

Phone   (02) 9558-3332
Fax   (02) 9559-5797
Freecall 1800-646-013
E-mail   *kriskindlguesthouse@hotmail.com*
Internet *www.guesthousesydney.com*

Blue Mountains

The Blue Mountains are only a short distance from Sydney and are a popular destination after first arriving in Australia and checking out Sydney. Travelers are impressed by the spectacular views, including the famous '3 sisters' rock formation, waterfalls, and a large number bushwalking tracks which offer a more in-depth experience. Also nearby are the incredible Jenolan Caves, and a variety of activities such as rock climbing, mountain biking and more.

Katoomba Mountain Lodge

31 Lurline St
Katoomba NSW 2780

Phone   (02) 4782-3933
Fax   (02) 4782-3978
Freecall 1800-800-678
E-mail   *kmtlodge@pnc.com.au*
Internet *www.bluemts.com.au/kmtlodge*

Number 14

14 Lovel St
Katoomba NSW 2780

Phone   (02) 4782-7104
E-mail   *no14@lisp.com.au*
Internet *www.bluemts.com.au/no14*

Clarendon Guesthouse

68 Lurline St
Katoomba NSW 2780

Phone   (02) 4782-1322
Fax   (02) 4782-2564
E-mail   *clarendon@pnc.com.au*
Internet *www.clarendonguesthouse.com.au*

Gardners Inn

255 Great Western Highway
Katoomba NSW 2780

Phone   (02) 4787-8347
Fax   (02) 4787-7725
E-mail   *info@gardnersinn.com.au*
Internet *www.gardnersinn.com.au*

Blue Mountains Katoomba Backpackers

190 Bathurst Rd
Katoomba NSW 2780

Phone   (02) 4782-4226
Fax   (02) 4782-4236
Freecall 1800-624-226
E-mail   *bmb@kacadventures.com*
Internet *www.kacadventures.com/bmb*

Blue Mountains YHA

207 Katoomba St
Katoomba NSW 2780

Phone   (02) 4782-1416
Fax   (02) 4782-6203
E-mail   *bluemountains@yhansw.org.au*
Internet *www.yha.org.au*

Coffs Harbour

For Australians, Coffs Harbour is a popular holiday destination due to the laid-back atmosphere, entertainment and oceans sports. That's why Russell Crowe owns a ranch here! It's also a favorite destination with backpackers. Surfing, sea kayaking and diving are popular. Don't miss the Big Banana!

Hoey Moey Backpackers

Ocean Parade
Coffs Harbour NSW 2450

Phone   (02) 6651-7966
Fax   (02) 6651-4434
Freecall 1800-683-322
E-mail   *hoey@hoeymoey.com.au*
Internet *www.hoeymoey.com.au*

Aussitel Backpackers
312 High St
Coffs Harbour NSW 2450

Phone   (02) 6651-1871
Fax   (02) 6651-5335
Freecall 1800-330-335
E-mail   *info@aussitel.com*
Internet *www.aussitel.com*

Barracuda Backpackers

19 Arthur St
Coffs Harbour NSW 2450

Phone   (02) 6651-3514
Fax   (02) 6651-4575
Freecall 1800-111-514
E-mail   *barracuda@coffs.tv*
Internet *www.backpackers.coffs.tv*

Coffs Harbour YHA Backpackers Resort

110 Albany St
Coffs Harbour NSW 2450

Phone   (02) 6652-6462
Fax   (02) 6652-6462
E-mail   *coffsyha@ozemail.com.au*
Internet *www.yha.org.au*

Byron Bay

Byron Bay is the 'alternative capital' of Australia, and is one of the most popular backpacker spots due to the wide variety of entertainment for people of all tastes. In fact, it can almost be guaranteed that you will stay here longer than you had intended, it is inevitable! The alternative part of the experience consists of fire-twirling and dreadlocks, yoga and crystals, drumming and didgeridoos - you can even make your own! For travelers without such alternative tastes, Byron offers great beaches, lots of sun, surfing, sea kayaking, and more great sun and beaches! Also don't miss a trip to the Lighthouse for sunrise.

Aquarius Backpackers Motel

16 Lawson St
Byron Bay NSW 2481

Phone   (02) 6685-7663
Fax   (02) 6685-7439
Freecall 1800-028-909
E-mail   *aquarius@aquarius-backpackers.com.au*
Internet *www.aquarius-backpackers.com.au*

Arts Factory Lodge
Skinners Shoot Rd
Byron Bay NSW 2481
Phone   (02) 6685-7709
Fax   (02) 6685-8534
E-mail   *info@artsfactory.com.au*
Internet *www.artsfactory.com.au*

Belongil Beachouse
Childe St
Byron Bay NSW 2481
Phone   (02) 6685-7868
Fax   (02) 6685-7445
Freecall 1-800-880-020
E-mail   *info@belongilbeachouse.com*
Internet *www.belongilbeachouse.com*

J's Bay YHA

7 Carlyle St
Byron Bay NSW 2481

Phone   (02) 6685-8853
Fax   (02) 6685-6766
Freecall 1800-678-195
E-mail   *jbay@nor.com.au*
Internet *www.byron-bay.com/jsbay*

Byron Bay Bunkhouse

1 Carlyle St
Byron Bay NSW 2481

Phone   (02) 6685-8311
Fax   (02) 6685-8258
Freecall 1800-241-600
E-mail   *byronbay@nrg.com.au*
Internet *www.byronbay-bunkhouse.com.au*

Cape Byron Hostel YHA

Corner Byron & Middleton Sts
Byron Bay NSW 2481

Phone   (02) 6685-8788
Fax   (02) 6685-8814
Freecall 1800-652-627
E-mail   *byronyha@nrg.com.au*
Internet *www.nrg.com.au/byronyha*

North Coast

There are many interesting backpacker-friendly towns along the north coast of New South Wales, all of which are easy to visit while traveling north from Sydney or south from Brisbane. Among the most popular attractions are the endless secluded beaches, many with great surfing, but also each town offers it's own atmosphere and attractions so be sure to explore as many as possible...

Ballina Travellers Lodge YHA

36 Tamar St
Ballina NSW 2478

Phone   (02) 6686-6737
Fax   (02) 6686-6342
E-mail   *lenballina@ozemail.com.au*
Internet *www.tropicalnsw.com.au/ballinayha*

Bellingen YHA Backpackers

2 Short St
Bellingen NSW 2454

Phone   (02) 6655-1116
Fax   (02) 6655-1358
E-mail *belloyha@midcoast.com.au*
Internet *www.midcoast.com.au/~belloyha*

Emu Park Lodge

77 Coast Rd
Cabarita Beach NSW 2488

Phone   (02) 6676-1190
Fax   (02) 6676-1190
E-mail *emupark@norex.com.au*

Dolphin Lodge YHA

43 Head St
Forster NSW 2428

Phone   (02) 6555-8155
Fax   (02) 6555-8155
Freecall 1800-807-766
E-mail *dolphin_lodge@hotmail.com*
Internet *www.yha.org.au*

Lennox Head Beachouse YHA

3 Ross St
Lennox Head NSW 2478

Phone   (02) 6687-7636
Fax   (02) 6687-7739
E-mail   *lennoxbacpac@hotmail.com*

Lismore Backpackers

14 Ewing St
Lismore NSW 2480

Phone   (02) 6621-6118
Fax   (02) 6622-8422
E-mail   *currendi@nor.com.au*
Internet *www.lismorebackpackers.com*

Riverside YHA Backpackers

1 Tumbulgum Rd
Murwillumbah NSW 2484

Phone   (02) 6672-3763
E-mail   *mbahyha@norex.com.au*
Internet
nnsw.worldtourism.com.au/RiversideBackpackers

Murwillumbah Hotel

13 Wharf St
Murwillumbah NSW 2484

Phone   (02) 6672-1139
Fax   (02) 6672-7219
E-mail   *info@murwillumbahhotel.com.au*
Internet *www.murwillumbahhotel.com.au*

Nambucca Heads Backpackers

3 Newman St
Nambucca Heads NSW 2448

Phone   (02) 6568-6360
Fax   (02) 6568-5984
Freecall 1800-630-663
E-mail   *jpilgrim@midcoast.com.au*
Internet *www.midcoast.com.au/~jpilgrim*

Nimbin Rox YHA

74 Thorburn St
Nimbin NSW 2480

Phone   (02) 6689-0022
Fax   (02) 6689-0022
E-mail   *nimbinrox@hotmail.com*
Internet *www.nimbinroxhostel.com*

Ozzie Pozzie Backpackers

36 Waugh St
Port Macquarie NSW 2444

Phone   (02) 6583-8133
Fax   (02) 6583-8133
Freecall 1800-620-020
E-mail   *ozziepozzie@bigpond.com*
Internet *www.nomadsworld.com/oz*

Port Macquarie YHA
40 Church St
Port Macquarie NSW 2444

Phone   (02) 6583-5512
Fax   (02) 6583-5512
Freecall 1800-880-008
E-mail   *portmacquarie@yhansw.org.au*
Internet *www.yha.org.au*

Lindel Port Macquarie Backpackers

2 Hastings River Drive
Port Macquarie NSW 2444

Phone   (02) 3583-1791
Fax   (02) 3583-1791
Freecall 1800-688-882
E-mail   *lindel@midcoast.com.au*

Pacific Hotel

18 Pilot St
Yamba NSW 2463

Phone   (02) 6646-2466
Fax   (02) 6646-2662
E-mail   *pachotel@nor.com.au*
Internet *www.gdaypubs.com.au/pacifichotelyamba*

South Coast

The coast south of Sydney is full of beaches, surfing, National Parks, bushwalking and more. Areas such as Bateman's Bay, Merimbula and Ulladulla are popular spots to stay along the way as you head south. Whitewater rafting and diving are also available at many locations for the more adventurous traveler.

Batemans Bay Shady Willows YHA

Corner Old Princes Highway & South St
Batemans Bay NSW 2536

Phone   (02) 4472-4972
Fax   (02) 4472-4045
E-mail   *info@shadywillows.com.au*
Internet *www.shadywillows.com.au*

Beach Road Backpackers Hostel

92 Beach Rd
Batemans Bay NSW 2536

Phone   (02) 4472-3644
Fax   (02) 4472-7208
E-mail   *brbph@austarnet.com.au*

Manna Park Hostel

Redhill Rd, off Sapphire Coast Drive
Merimbula NSW 2548

Phone   (02) 6495-0063
Fax   (02) 6495-0013
E-mail   *mannapark@mannapark.com.au*
Internet *www.mannapark.com.au*

Wandarrah Lodge YHA

8 Marine Parade
Merimbula NSW 2548

Phone   (02) 6495-3503
Fax   (02) 6495-3163
E-mail   *wanlodge@asitis.com.au*
Internet *www.wandarrahlodge.com.au*

Narooma Blue YHA

8 Princes Highway
Narooma NSW 2546

Phone   (02) 4476-4440
Fax   (02) 4476-5444
E-mail   *naroomayha@narooma.com*
Internet *www.yha.org.au*

M&M's Guesthouse
1a Scenic Drive
Nowra NSW 2541

Phone   (02) 4422-8006
Fax   (02) 4422-8007
E-mail   *mmguesthouse@mail2me.com.au*
Internet *www.mmguesthouse.com*

South Coast Backpackers

63 Princes Highway
Ulladulla NSW 2539

Phone   (02) 4454-0500
E-mail   *scbackpackers@shoalhaven.net.au*
Internet *www.southcoastbackpackers.com.au*

Beach n Bush

57 St Georges Avenue
Vincentia NSW 2540

Phone (02) 4441-6880
Fax (02) 4441-6855
Freecall 1800-666-000
E-mail *info@beachnbush.com.au*
Internet *www.beachnbush.com.au*

Central Coast

Less than 200km north of Sydney is Newcastle, which has the 2nd highest population in New South Wales and is a major surfing and party destination. A little further north is Port Stephens, home to dolphins and sand-dune surfing. There are also plenty of other areas with beaches and other activities available to you as you travel up to the north coast.

Backpackers by the Beach

34-36 Hunter St
Newcastle NSW 2300

Phone (02) 4926-3472
Fax (02) 4926-5210
E-mail *backbeach@nobbys.net.au*
Internet *www.backpackersbythebeach.com.au*

Newcastle Beach YHA

30 Pacific St
Newcastle NSW 2300

Phone   (02) 4925 3544
Fax   (02) 4925 3944
E-mail   *mail@newcastleyha.com.au*
Internet *www.newcastleyha.com.au*

Backpackers Newcastle

42-44 Denison St
Newcastle NSW 2303

Phone   (02) 4969-3436
Fax   (02) 4940-8726
Freecall 1800-333-436
E-mail   *info@newcastlebackpackers.com*
Internet *www.newcastlebackpackers.com*

Samurai Beach Bungalows

Corner Frost Rd & Robert Connell Close
Anna Bay, Port Stephens NSW 2316

Phone   (02) 4982-1921
Fax   (02) 4982-1921
E-mail   *samurai@nelsonbay.com.au*
Internet *www.portstephens.org.au/samurai*

Shoal Bay Backpackers YHA

59-61 Shoal Bay Beachfront Rd
Shoal Bay NSW 2315

Phone   (02) 4981-0982
Fax   (02) 4984-1052
E-mail   *shoalbaymotel@bigpond.com*
Net *www.portstephens.org.au/shoalbaymotel-yha*

Stockton Beach Backpackers

68 Mitchell St
Stockton NSW 2295

Phone   (02) 4928-4333
Fax   (02) 4928-4522
E-mail
enquiries@stocktonbeachbackpackers.com.au
Internet *www.stocktonbeachbackpackers.com.au*

Terrigal Beach Lodge YHA

12 Campbell Crescent
Terrigal NSW 2260

Phone   (02) 4385-3330
Fax   (02) 4385-3330
E-mail   *yha@terrigalbeachlodge.com.au*
Internet *www.terrigalbeachlodge.com.au*

Other Areas

These areas are mostly inland, off the well-beaten track of the coast. There are many Farmstays where you can actually participate in the activities of a working farm. Jindabyne and Thredbo offer snow skiing in season, Tamworth is the home of country music, and Dubbo's 'Western Plains Zoo' offers one of the world's best open-range (no cages) animal viewing experiences, so don't miss these many interesting areas and all they have to show you about the 'real Australia'.

Bundanoon YHA

Railway Avenue
Bundanoon NSW 2578

Phone   (02) 4883-6010
Fax   (02) 4883-7470
E-mail   *bundyha@hinet.net.au*
Internet *www.yha.org.au*

Bunkhouse Backpackers

28-30 Soho St
Cooma NSW 2630

Phone   (02) 6452-2983
Fax   (02) 6452-2983
E-mail   *info@bunkhousemotel.com.au*
Internet *www.bunkhousemotel.com.au*

Dubbo Backpackers YHA

87 Brisbane St
Dubbo NSW 2830

Phone   (02) 6882-0922
Fax   (02) 6882-0922
E-mail   *yhadubbo@hwy.com.au*
Internet *www.yha.org.au*

Milbulla Farm Stay

Milbulla
Gunnedah NSW 2380

Phone   (02) 6743-7207
E-mail   *milbulla@northnet.com.au*
Internet *www.northnet.com.au/~milbulla*

Snowy Mountains Backpackers

7-8 Gippsland St
Jindabyne NSW 2626

Phone   (02) 6456-1500
Fax   (02) 6456-1511
Freecall 1800-333-468
E-mail   *backpack@snowy.net.au*
Internet *www.snowybackpackers.com.au*

Bogia Tank Farm

Mt Daylight Rd
Lake Cargelligo NSW 2672

Phone   (02) 6896-9837
Fax   (02) 6896-9807
E-mail   *pborella@bigpond.com*
Internet *www.bogiatank.com.au*

Dag Sheep Station

Crawney Rd
Nundle NSW 2340

Phone   (02) 6769-3234
E-mail   *info@thedag.com.au*
Internet *www.thedag.com.au*

Castle Mountain Farmstay

Castle Mountain
Quirindi NSW 2343

Phone   (02) 6746-2102
E-mail   *castlem@northnet.com.au*
Internet *www.northnet.com.au/~castlem*

Scone YHA

1151 Segenhoe Rd
Scone NSW 2337

Phone   (02) 6545-2072
Fax   (02) 6545-9288
E-mail   *yhascone@hunterlink.net.au*
Internet *www.yha.org.au*

Tamworth YHA

169 Marius St
Tamworth NSW 2340

Phone   (02) 6761-2600
Fax   (02) 6761-2002
E-mail   *tam_yha@yahoo.com.au*
Internet *www.yha.org.au*

Tenterfield Backpackers Lodge

2 Manners St
Tenterfield NSW 2372

Phone   (02) 6736-1477
Fax   (02) 6736-3552
E-mail   *tenterfieldlodge@ozemail.com.au*
Internet *www.tenterfieldbiz.com/tenterfieldlodge*

Thredbo YHA

8 Jack Adams Pathway
Thredbo NSW 2625

Phone   (02) 6457-6376
Fax   (02) 6457-6043
E-mail   *thredbo@yhansw.org.au*
Internet *www.ciau.com.au/YHA/thredbo.htm*

Nomads Cryon

Kamilaroi Highway
Walgett NSW 2832

Phone   (02) 6828-5237
Fax   (02) 6828-5211
E-mail   *contact@nomadscryon.com*
Internet *www.nomadscryon.com*

Canberra - A.C.T.

Many non-Australians mistakenly believe that Sydney is the capital of Australia. Sydney has the highest population, but it's not the capital. Canberra is the true capital and is located in the 'Australian Capital Territory' (ACT) which is a relatively small 'state' within New South Wales. Canberra and the surrounding areas offer a lot of interesting bushwalking, in fact it's not uncommon to see kangaroos in the parks right in Canberra due to the large amount of bushland surrounding the capital. Attractions include a free tour of the $1 billion Parliament House (complete with a grass roof!), visits to Lake Burley Griffith, the National Museum and National Gallery, and viewing the unique architecture of the many embassies from other countries. There are plenty of other activities here also, including a variety of nightlife and clubs.

Griffith International Hostel

112 Binya St
Griffith ACT 2603

Phone   (02) 6964-4236
Fax   (02) 6964-0080
E-mail   *info@griffithinternational.com.au*
Internet *www.griffithinternational.com.au*

Victor Lodge

29 Dawes St
Kingston ACT 2604

Phone   (02) 6295-7777
Fax   (02) 6295-2466
E-mail   *contact@victorlodge.com.au*
Internet *www.victorlodge.com.au*

City Walk Hotel

2 Mort St
Canberra ACT 2601

Phone   (02) 6257-0124
Fax   (02) 6257-0116
Freecall 1800-600-124
E-mail   *citywalk@ozemail.com.au*
Internet *www.citywalkhotel.com.au*

Canberra City Backpackers

7 Akuna St
Canberra City ACT 2600

Phone   (02) 6257-3999
Fax   (02) 6257-3955
Freecall 1800-300-488
E-mail   *info@canberracityaccommodation.com.au*
Internet *www.canberrabackpackers.net.au*

Canberra YHA

191 Dryandra St
O'Connor ACT 2602

Phone   (02) 6248-9155
Fax   (02) 6249-1731
E-mail   *canberra@yhansw.org.au*
Internet *www.yha.org.au*

Northern Territory (NT)

The Northern Territory is an amazing place, from the tropical north to the 'Red Centre'. In fact there's no other place on Earth quite like it. Uluru (temporarily named Ayers Rock by the Europeans) is at the heart of Australia, and the whole area heading up to Darwin at the top of the NT offers so many attractions that it would be difficult to see everything, but you have to try!

Both the modern city of Darwin and the more outback city of Alice Springs offer a range of attractions, and serve as great starting points for organizing trips to any of the territory's sights such as Kings Canyon, the Devil's Marbles, the natural thermal river of Mataranka... Just the beginning of your outback adventure! Remember, much of this area is desert and the heat can be extreme, so some travelers prefer the cooler months for a more comfortable experience.

Darwin

Darwin is the capital of the Northern Territory, right at the top of the state. Darwin is a well-placed start (or end) point for your travels to (or from) the 'Red Centre', Kakadu National Park, the East Coast, and even South-East Asia. Darwin is a beautiful tropical town where travelers tend to feel at home immediately. Attractions here include Crocodylus Park, the Art Gallery and Museum, beaches and diving. And most of all, the laid-back welcoming atmosphere.

Gecko Lodge

146 Mitchell St
Darwin NT 0800

Phone   (08) 8981-2733
Fax   (08) 8981-3680
Freecall 1800-811-250
E-mail   *austour@ozemail.com.au*
Internet *www.geckolodge.com.au*

Banyan View Lodge

119 Mitchell St
Darwin NT 0800

Phone   (08) 8981-8644
Fax   (08) 8981-6104
E-mail   *ywcadwn_bvl@optusnet.com.au*
Internet *members.optusnet.com.au/~ywcaofdarwin*

Elke's Inner City Backpackers Lodge

112 Mitchell St
Darwin NT 0800

Phone   (08) 8981-8399
Fax   (08) 8981-4401
Freecall 1800-816-302
E-mail   *info@elkesbackpackers.com.au*
Internet *www.elkesbackpackers.com.au*

Frogshollow Backpackers

27 Lindsay St
Darwin NT 0800

Phone   (08) 8941-2600
Fax   (08) 8941-0758
Freecall 1800-068-686
E-mail   *book@frogs-hollow.com.au*
Internet *www.frogs-hollow.com.au*

Globetrotters Lodge

97 Mitchell St
Darwin NT 0800

Phone   (08) 8981-5385
Fax   (08) 8981-9096
Freecall 1800-800-798
E-mail   *info@globetrotters.com.au*
Internet *www.globetrotters.com.au*

Melaleuca Backpackers Resort

50 Mitchell St
Darwin NT 0800

Phone   (08) 8956-1091
Fax   (08) 8941-3368
Freecall 1800-623-543
E-mail   *info@southernlodges.com.au*
Internet *www.southernlodges.com.au*

Wilderness Lodge Backpackers

88 Mitchell St
Darwin NT 0800

Phone   (08) 8981-8363
Fax   (08) 8941-3360
Freecall 1800-068-886
E-mail   *info@wildlodge.com.au*
Internet *www.wildlodge.com.au*

Darwin International YHA

69 Mitchell St
Darwin NT 0800

Phone   (08) 8981-3995
Fax   (08) 8981-6674
E-mail   *darwinyha@yhant.org.au*
Internet *www.yha.org.au*

YMCA

The Esplanade, Doctors Gully
Darwin NT 0801

Phone   (08) 8981-8377
Fax   (08) 8941-0288
E-mail   *ymcadrw@ozemail.com.au*
Internet *www.ozemail.com.au/~ymcadrw*

The Cavenagh

12 Cavenagh St
Darwin NT 0801

Phone   (08) 8941-6383
Fax   (08) 8941-4541
E-mail   *sales@thecavenagh.com*
Internet *www.thecavenagh.com*

Barramundi Lodge

4 Gardens Rd, The Gardens
Darwin NT 0820

Phone   (08) 8941-6466
Fax   (08) 8942-3883
E-mail   *barramundilodge@bigpond.com*
Internet *www.barramundilodge.com.au*

Alice Springs

Alice is the perfect base from which to explore all the different areas around the 'Red Centre' of Australia, so named because of the abundance of red earth going as far as the eye can see in every direction. From Alice you can easily organize trips to Uluru (Ayers Rock), Kings Canyon, The Olgas and all the popular and spectacularly beautiful natural attractions of this area. Be sure to stay in Alice for at least a few days to soak up the atmosphere, and the Aboriginal culture, before trekking into the wilderness...

Elke's Backpacker Resort

39 Gap Rd
Alice Springs NT 0870

Phone   (08) 8952-8422
Fax   (08) 8952-8143
Freecall 1800-633-354
E-mail *info@elkes.com.au*
Internet *www.elkes.com.au*

Alice Lodge Backpackers

4 Mueller St
Alice Springs NT 0870

Phone   (08) 8953-7975
Fax   (08) 8953-0804
Freecall 1800-351-925
E-mail *alice_lodge@hotmail.com*
Internet *www.langwith.com/Alice_Lodge*

Melanka Resort

94 Todd St
Alice Springs NT 0870

Phone   (08) 8952-4744
Fax   (08) 8952-4587
Freecall 1800-815-066
E-mail   *backpackers@melanka.com.au*
Internet *www.melanka.com.au*

Ossie's Backpackers

18 Warburton St
Alice Springs NT 0870

Phone   (08) 8952-2308
Fax   (08) 8952-2211
Freecall 1800-628-211
E-mail   *ossies@ossies.com.au*
Internet *www.ossies.com.au*

Toddy's Hostel

41 Gap Rd
Alice Springs NT 0870

Phone   (08) 8952-1322
Fax   (08) 8952-1767
Freecall 1800-806-240
E-mail   *toddys@toddys.com.au*
Internet *www.toddys.com.au*

Pioneer YHA Hostel
Corner Parsons St & Leichhardt Terrace
Alice Springs NT 0870

Phone   (08) 8952-8855
Fax   (08) 8952-4144

E-mail   *alicepioneer@yhant.org.au*
Internet *www.yha.org.au*

Desert Rose Inn

15 Railway Terrace
Alice Springs NT 0870

Phone   (08) 8952-1411
Fax   (08) 8952-3232
E-mail   *info@desertroseinn.com.au*
Internet *www.desertroseinn.com.au*

Annies Place

4 Traeger Avenue
Alice Springs NT 0870

Phone   (08) 8952-1545
Fax   (08) 8952-8280
Freecall 1800-359-089
E-mail   *info@mulgas.com.au*
Internet *www.mulgas.com.au/annies.html*

Other Areas

There's no way to describe the absolutely incredible beauty of the Australian Outback. There is so much to see and experience, and you probably won't be able to visit it all - but it's worth the effort to try and you definitely won't ever forget your time here. The most obvious landmark here is Ayers Rock which has been re-named to it's original Aboriginal title, Uluru, but it's just the beginning, with Kings Canyon's amazing cliffs and Garden of Eden, the rock formations of The Olgas and the Devil's Marbles, the thermal pools and river of Mataranka, and the truely outback experience of Tennant Creek, and still it's just the start of your adventure!

Outback Pioneer YHA Lodge

Ayers Rock Resort
Uluru (Ayers Rock) NT 0872

Phone   (08) 8957-7888
Fax   (08) 8957-7615
Freecall 1300-139-889
E-mail   *reservations@voyages.com.au*
Internet *www.voyages.com.au*

Palm Court YHA

Corner Third & Giles Sts
Katherine NT 0850

Phone   (08) 8972-2722
Fax   (08) 8971-1443
E-mail   *palmcourt1@bigpond.com*
Internet *www.yha.org.au*

Kookaburra Backpackers Lodge

Lindsay St
Katherine NT 0851

Phone   (08) 8971-0257
Fax   (08) 8972-1567
Freecall 1800-808-211
E-mail   *kookaburra@nt-tech.com.au*
Internet *www.inspirit.com.au/Kookaburra*

Katherine River Lodge

50 Giles St
Katherine NT 0851

Phone   (08) 8971-0266
E-mail   *mail@katherineriverlodge.net*
Internet *www.katherineriverlodge.net*

Victoria Lodge

21 Victoria Highway
Katherine NT 0851

Phone   (08) 8972-3464
Fax   (08) 8971-1738
Freecall 1800-808-875
E-mail   *victorialodge@bigpond.com*

Mount Bundy Station

Haynes Rd
Adelaide River NT 0846

Phone   (08) 8976-7009
Fax   (08) 8976-7113
E-mail *mt.bundy@octa4.net.au*

Glen Helen Resort

Namatjira Drive, via Alice Springs
Glen Helen NT 0870

Phone   (08) 8956-7489
Fax   (08) 8956-7495
Freecall 1800-896-110
E-mail *res@glenhelen.com.au*
Internet *www.southernlodges.com.au*

Gagudju Lodge YHA

Cooinda, off Kakadu Highway
Kakadu National Park 0886

Phone   (08) 8979-0145
Fax   (08) 8979-0148
E-mail *reservations@gagudjulodgecooinda.com.au*
Internet *www.gagudjulodgecooinda.com.au*

Kings Canyon YHA

Ernest Giles Rd, Watarrka National Park
Kings Canyon NT 0872

Phone   (08) 8956-7442
Fax   (08) 8956-7410
Freecall 1800-817-622
E-mail   *reservations@voyages.com.au*
Internet *www.voyages.com.au*

Mary River YHA

Arnhem Highway
Mary River NT 0850

Phone   (08) 8978-8877
Fax   (08) 8978-8899
E-mail   *general@maryriverpark.com.au*
Internet *www.maryriverpark.com.au*

Mataranka Homestead

Homestead Rd
Mataranka NT 0852

Phone   (08) 8975-4544
Fax   (08) 8975-4580
Freecall 1800-754-544
E-mail   *matarankahomestead@bigpond.com.au*

Tourist's Rest Youth Hostel

Corner Windley & Leichardt Sts
Tennant Creek NT 0860

Phone   (08) 8962-2719
Fax   (08) 8962-2718
E-mail   *tonyjohn@swtch.com.au*
Internet *www.touristrest.com.au*

Safari Backpackers YHA

12 Davidson St
Tennant Creek NT 0860

Phone   (08) 8962-2207
Fax   (08) 8962-3188
E-mail   *safari@swtch.com.au*
Internet *www.yha.org.au*

Queensland (QLD)

Queensland is known as the 'Sunshine State', but the sunshine is not the only reason that there are more hostels here than any other state - it's because there is SO much to see and experience.

If you're coming from the south, you'll first come to the Gold Coast, just across the border from New South Wales. The Gold Coast is one of the major tourist spots of Australia, and some backpackers love the glitz and glamor while others can't wait to move on to something more 'real'. Brisbane, the capital of Queensland, is just north of the Gold Coast yet is almost the opposite, being one of Australia's most laid-back major cities.

Heading north you'll come to the Sunshine Coast, great beaches, water sports, and there's surely plenty here to please everyone. Don't miss the Crocodile Hunter's own zoo here! Traveling further north you'll come to central Queensland, beautiful islands and bays, whales, and the real 'country experience'. Then back to partying and adventure in Airlie Beach, the highlight of many backpacker's trips and truly a Paradise. The Great Barrier Reef also follows along much of the Queensland Coast and is accessible from many of the coastal towns.

You really should relax in beautiful Mission Beach, Townsville or Magnetic Island before heading further north to Cairns, where partying and wild adventures may again be inevitable! There's also plenty of unique experiences awaiting you in the surrounding Far North Queensland areas, and finally Cape Tribulation is the farthest north you can go with regular vehicles - and the scenery is well worth the trip.

Brisbane

Brisbane is the capital of Queensland and is a big city, but with a more laid-back atmosphere and lower costs that many major cities. A short walk just over a bridge from the city centre will lead you to Southbank Parklands, a true oasis and not only a great place to relax but also to swim in the man-made yet beautiful lagoon/beach. Also nearby is the Cultural Centre with a good free museum and art gallery.

The Mt Coot-tha lookout and gardens offer a great perspective of the whole city and are worth a visit. A little farther is the famous Lone Pine koala sanctuary which houses over 100 koalas, and is also a great place to hand-feed kangaroos.

Apart from the city itself, there are other places to stay which are only a short walk from the center of the action. One very popular area is the always groovy Fortitude Valley ('the Valley') with great nightlife, although it is a red-light area and can be too much for some travelers (though it's a less obvious than Kings Cross in Sydney). More quiet and just a little further from the city is New Farm. West End offers a more bohemian alternative atmosphere.

Banana Bender Backpackers

118 Petrie Terrace
Brisbane QLD 4000

Phone   (07) 3367-1157
Fax   (07) 3368-1047
Freecall 1800-241-157
E-mail   *bbenders@bigpond.net.au*
Internet *www.bananabenders.com*

Palace Backpackers

Corner Ann & Edward Sts
Brisbane QLD 4000

Phone   (07) 3211-2433
Fax   (07) 3211-2466
Freecall 1800-676-340
E-mail   *brisbane@palacebackpackers.com.au*
Internet *www.palacebackpackers.com.au*

Tinbilly Travellers

462 George St
Brisbane QLD 4000

Phone   (07) 3238-5888
Freecall 1800-446-646
E-mail   *reservations@tinbilly.com*
Internet *www.tinbilly.com*

Brisbane City Backpackers

380 Upper Roma St
Brisbane QLD 4000

Phone   (07) 3211-3221
Freecall 1800-062-572
E-mail   *info@citybackpackers.com*
Internet *www.citybackpackers.com*

Prince Consort Backpackers

230 Wickham St
Fortitude Valley QLD 4006

Phone   (07) 3257-2252
Fax   (07) 3252-4130
Freecall 1800-225-005
E-mail   *pcbakpak@bigpond.net.au*
Internet *www.nomadsworld.com/oz*

Tourist Guest House

555 Gregory Terrace
Fortitude Valley QLD 4006

Phone   (07) 3252-4171
Fax   (07) 3252-2704
Freecall 1800-800-589
E-mail   *tourist_guest_house@yahoo.com.au*
Internet *www.touristguesthouse.com.au*

Reef O

14-20 Constance St
Fortitude Valley QLD 4006

Phone   (07) 3252-2565
Fax   (07) 3854-0264
Freecall 1800-173-336
E-mail   *info@reefos.com.au*
Internet *www.reefos.com.au*

Durham Villa Backpackers

17 Laura St
Highgate Hill QLD 4101

Phone   (07) 3844-6853
E-mail   *durhamvilla@hotmail.com*
Internet *www.durhamvillabackpackers.com*

Globetrekkers

35 Balfour St
New Farm QLD 4005

Phone   (07) 3358-1251
E-mail   *hostel@globetrekkers.net*
Internet *www.globetrekkers.net*

Brisbane Backpackers Resort

110 Vulture St
West End QLD 4101

Phone   (07) 3844-9956
Fax   (07) 3844-9295
Freecall 1800-626-452
E-mail   *brisbanebackpackers@yahoo.com.au*
Internet
www.home.aone.net.au/brisbanebackpackers

Somewhere to Stay Backpackers

Corner Brighton Rd & Franklin St
West End QLD 4101

Phone   (07) 3844-6093
Fax   (07) 3846-4584
Freecall 1800-812-398
E-mail   *reception@somewheretostay.com.au*
Internet *www.somewheretostay.com.au*

Near Brisbane

There are many islands and bays just a short distance from Brisbane, offering a wide range of water activities such as diving, snorkelling, surfing, wind surfing, as well as bushwalking and more. These places also tend to be less 'touristy' than many other areas of the coast.

Moreton Bay Lodge

45 Cambridge Parade
Manly Harbour Village QLD 4179

Phone   (07) 3396-3020
Fax   (07) 3396-1355
Freecall 1800-800-157
E-mail   *info@moretonbaylodge.com.au*
Internet *www.moretonbaylodge.com.au*

Canoeworld Lodge

Sandy Beach
Russell Island QLD 4184

Phone   (07) 3409-1960
E-mail   *trev@canoeworld.com*

Stradbroke Island Guesthouse

1 Eastcoast Rd, Point Lookout
Stradbroke Island QLD 4183

Phone   (07) 3409-8888
Fax   (07) 3409-8588
E-mail   *info@stradbrokeislandscuba.com.au*
Internet *www.stradbrokeislandscuba.com.au*

The Gold Coast

The Gold Coast is over 30km of beaches running from the border of NSW up towards Brisbane. This area is one of Australia's most popular holiday locations, and that means it's also extremely touristy - expect bright flashing lights and tacky t-shirts! The main tourist suburb is 'Surfers Paradise', and it's party central for backpackers. The beaches in Surfers Paradise are often packed with swimmers and surfers on weekends and during holidays, but you can also find quieter beaches if you walk a little more north or south. Springbrook is a beautiful rainforest in the mountains of the Gold Coast hinterland. Also nearby are the major entertainment parks Dream World, Movie World, Sea World and more.

Backpackers in Paradise

40 Peninsular Drive
Surfers Paradise QLD 4217

Phone   (07) 5538-4344
Fax   (07) 5538-4344
Freecall 1800-268-621
E-mail *BackpackersinParadise@magicplanet.net*
Internet *www.backpackersinparadise.com*

Sunset Court

Corner Watson Esplanade & Peninsular Drive
Surfers Paradise QLD 4217

Phone   (07) 5539-0266
Fax   (07) 5561-0691
E-mail *austour@connect.net.au*
Internet *www.goldcoast-holidays.com*

Islander Backpackers Resort

6 Beach Rd
Surfers Paradise QLD 4217

Phone   (07) 5538-8000
Fax   (07) 5592-2762
Freecall 1800-074-393
E-mail   *info@parkregis.com.au*
Internet *www.parkregis.com.au*

Sleeping Inn Surfers

26 Peninsular Drive
Surfers Paradise QLD 4217

Phone   (07) 5592-4455
Fax   (07) 5592-5266
Freecall 1800-817-832
E-mail   *info@sleepinginn.com.au*
Internet *www.sleepinginn.com.au*

Surfers Paradise Backpackers Resort

2837 Gold Coast Highway
Surfers Paradise QLD 4217

Phone   (07) 5592-4677
Fax   (07) 5531-5835
Freecall 1800-282-800
E-mail   *spbr@surfersparadisebackpackers.com.au*
Internet *www.surfersparadisebackpackers.com.au*

Surf N Sun Beachside Backpackers

3323 Gold Coast Highway
Surfers Paradise QLD 4217

Phone   (07) 5592-2363
Fax   (07) 5592-2348
Freecall 1800-678-194
E-mail   *info@surfnsun-goldcoast.com*
Internet *www.surfnsun-goldcoast.com*

Cheers Backpackers

8 Pine Avenue
Surfers Paradise QLD 4217

Phone   (07) 5531-6539
Fax   (07) 5539-0563
Freecall 1800-636-539
E-mail   *cheersbackpackers@hotmail.com*

Gold Coast International Backpackers Resort

28 Hamilton Avenue
Surfers Paradise QLD 4217

Phone   (07) 5592-5888
Fax   (07) 5538-9310
Freecall 1800-123-030
E-mail   *bookings@goldcoastbackpackers.com.au*
Internet *www.goldcoastbackpackers.com.au*

British Arms International Backpackers YHA

70 Seaworld Drive, Mariners Cove
Main Beach QLD 4217

Phone   (07) 5571-1776
Fax   (07) 5571-1747
Freecall 1800-680-269
E-mail   *info@britisharms.com.au*
Internet *www.britisharms.com.au*

Trekkers Backpacker's Resort

22 White St
Southport QLD 4215

Phone   (07) 5591-5616
Fax   (07) 5591-5616
Freecall 1800-100-004
E-mail   *trekkers@omcs.com.au*
Internet *www.trekkersbackpackers.com*

Aquarius Backpackers

44 Queen St
Southport QLD 4217

Phone   (07) 5527-1300
Fax   (07) 5561-1177
Freecall 1800-229-955
E-mail   *info@aquariusbackpackers.com.au*
Internet *www.aquariusbackpackers.com.au*

Coolangatta/Kirra Beach YHA

230 Coolangatta Rd
Bilinga QLD 4225

Phone   (07) 5536-7644
Fax   (07) 5599-5436
E-mail   *booking@coolangattayha.com*
Internet *www.yha.org.au*

Sunset Strip Budget Resort

199 Boundary St
Coolangatta QLD 4225

Phone   (07) 5599-5517
Fax   (07) 5536-7566
E-mail   *holiday@sunsetstrip.com.au*
Internet *www.sunsetstrip.com.au*

Springbrook Mountain Lodge YHA

317 Repeater Station Rd
Springbrook QLD 4213

Phone   (07) 5533-5366
Fax   (07) 5533-5366
E-mail   *springbrooklodge@ion.tm*
Internet *www.yha.org.au*

The Sunshine Coast

The Sunshine Coast is a long series of beaches and towns north of Brisbane, and is generally a lot more leisurely than the fast-paced Gold Coast south of Brisbane. Most of the Sunshine Coast offers a wide range of water sports, surfing, and other entertainment, activities and relaxation. Caloundra is located at the southern end of the Sunshine Coast, closest to Brisbane. Maroochydore is at the heart of the Sunshine Coast, and the great Underwater World is here. Nearby is the Big Pineapple, and Australia Zoo, the home of TV's 'Crocodile Hunter' - Steve Irwin. Noosa is a major town further north, and at the top of the Sunshine Coast is Rainbow Beach.

Caloundra City Backpackers

84 Omrah Avenue
Caloundra QLD 4551

Phone (07) 5499-7655
Fax (07) 5499-7644
E-mail *info@caloundracitybackpackers.com.au*
Internet *www.caloundracitybackpackers.com.au*

The Anchorage

18 Bowman Rd
Caloundra QLD 4551

Phone (07) 5491-1499
Fax (07) 5491-7279
Freecall 1800-626-299
E-mail *anchor@bigpond.net.au*

Suncoast Backpackers Lodge

50 Parker St
Maroochydore QLD 4558

Phone   (07) 5443-7544
E-mail   *vip_suncoast@hotmail.com*

Cotton Tree Beachouse

15 The Esplanade
Maroochydore QLD 4558

Phone   (07) 5443-1755
Fax   (07) 5451-0978
E-mail   *staff@cottontreebackpackers.com*
Internet *www.cottontreebackpackers.com*

Maroochydore YHA

24 Schirrmann Drive
Maroochydore QLD 4558

Phone   (07) 5443-3151
Fax   (07) 5479-3156
E-mail   *mail@yhabackpackers.com*
Internet *www.yhabackpackers.com*

Longboarders Lodge

10 Memorial Avenue
Maroochydore QLD 4558

Phone   (07) 5443-2981
Fax   (07) 5443-7343
E-mail   *sunandsurf@longboarders.com.au*
Internet *www.nomadsworld.com/oz*

Noosa

Noosa is located near the top of the Sunshine Coast, and is very popular with both Overseas and Australian tourists. The atmosphere is more up-market and exclusive than most areas, with prices to match, although there are always cheaper options for backpackers. The beaches and especially the National Park here are definitely worth a visit. There are also plenty of activities such as water-sports and horse-riding available.

Koala Beach Resort

44 Noosa Drive
Noosa Heads QLD 4567

Phone   (07) 5447-3355
Fax   (07) 5447-3893
Freecall 1800-466-444
E-mail   *backpackers-info@koalaresort.com.au*
Internet *www.koala-backpackers.com*

Halse Lodge YHA

2 Halse Lane
Noosa Heads QLD 4567

Phone   (07) 5447-3377
Fax   (07) 5447-2929
Freecall 1800-242-567
E-mail   *backpackers@halselodge.com.au*
Internet *www.halselodge.com.au*

Noosa Backpackers Resort

9-13 William St
Noosaville QLD 4566

Phone   (07) 5449-8151
Fax   (07) 5449-9408
Freecall 1800-626-673
E-mail   *paul@noosabackpackers.com*
Internet *www.noosabackpackers.com*

Noosa North Shore Retreat

Beach Rd
Tewantin QLD 4565

Phone   (07) 5447-1225
Freecall 1800-071-369
E-mail   *info@noosaretreat.com.au*
Internet *www.noosaretreat.com.au*

Gagaju Bush Camp

118 Johns Rd
Tewantin QLD 4565

Phone   (07) 5474-3522
Fax   (07) 5474-3522
Freecall 1300-302-271
E-mail   *gagajuinfo@yahoo.com*
Internet *www.travoholic.com/gagaju*

Rainbow Beach

Rainbow Beach is named for the colored sands which can be explored by 4-wheel drive tours or by a long walk. The sand cliffs along the beach have a wide variety of colors due to mineral content. Other attractions include a historical shipwreck that still sits on the beach, and an unusual naturally occurring sand tower named the 'Carlo Sandblow'. Rainbow Beach is also one of the 2 access points for Fraser Island (the other access point is Hervey Bay, see next section). Fraser Island is the world's largest sand island, and there are a wide range of things to see and do there, although a 4-wheel drive is necessary for travel around the island. Day-trips and self-drive tours are available.

Rainbow Beach Backpackers

66 Rainbow Beach Rd
Rainbow Beach QLD 4581

Phone   (07) 5486-3288
Fax   (07) 5486-3288
E-mail   *rainbowbeachback@excite.com*

Frasers on Rainbow

18 Spectrum Avenue
Rainbow Beach QLD 4581

Phone   (07) 5486-8885
Fax   (07) 5486-3317
Freecall 1800-100-170
E-mail *bookings@frasersonrainbow.com*
Internet *www.frasersonrainbow.com.au*

Rocks Backpackers Resort YHA

Spectrum St
Rainbow Beach QLD 4581

Phone   (07) 5486-3711
Fax   (07) 5486-3229
E-mail *rocksbackpackers@bigpond.com*
Internet *www.yha.org.au*

Dingos Rainbow Beach Hotel

Rainbow Beach Rd
Rainbow Beach QLD 4581

Phone   (07) 5486-8222
Fax   (07) 5486-8200
Freecall 1800-111-126
E-mail *accommodation@dingosatrainbow.com*
Internet *www.dingosatrainbow.com*

Hervey Bay

Hervey Bay is a laid-back town with a difference. Most obviously, the water is extremely calm, there are almost no waves due to the area being protected by Fraser Island off the coast. Some travelers are very grateful to be able to swim in the ocean here without the waves, although surfers will not be impressed! Also, the calm waters make it the ideal resting place for around 3000 whales every year as they migrate, this occurs only at certain times from August to November. Hervey Bay is also one of the 2 access points for Fraser Island (see the previous Rainbow Beach section for more information).

Boomerang Backpackers

335 The Esplanade
Hervey Bay QLD 4655

Phone   (07) 4128-4119
Freecall 1800-243-970
E-mail   *boomerangbackpackers@yahoo.com*
Internet *www.dkd.net/boomerang*

Colonial Backpackers YHA

820 Boat Harbour Drive
Hervey Bay QLD 4655

Phone   (07) 4125-1844
Fax   (07) 4125-3161
Freecall 1800-818-280
E-mail   *herveybay@bigpond.com.au*
Internet *www.coloniallogcabins.com*

Fraser Escape Backpackers

21 Denman Camp Rd, Scarness
Hervey Bay QLD 4655

Phone   (07) 4124-6237
Freecall 1800-646-888
E-mail   *escape@travel.ath.cx*
Internet *www.fraserescape.com.au*

Happy Wanderer Village

105 Truro St, Torquay
Hervey Bay QLD 4655

Phone   (07) 4125-1103
Fax   (07) 4125-3895
Freecall 1800-111-302
E-mail   *info@happywanderer.com.au*
Internet *www.happywanderer.com.au/backpackers*

Koala Beach Resort

408 The Esplanade
Hervey Bay QLD 4655

Phone   (07) 4125-3601
Fax   (07) 4125-3544
Freecall 1800-466-444
E-mail   *backpackers-info@koalaresort.com.au*
Internet *www.koala-backpackers.com*

Fraser Roving

412 The Esplanade
Hervey Bay QLD 4655

Phone   (07) 4125-6386
Fax   (07) 4125-3879
Freecall 1800-989-811
E-mail   *info@oziroving.com.au*
Internet *www.oziroving.com.au*

Beaches Backpackers

195 Torquay Rd, Torquay
Hervey Bay QLD 4655

Phone   (07) 4124-1322
Fax   (07) 4124-2727
Freecall 1800-655-501
E-mail   *herveybay@beaches.com.au*
Internet *www.beaches.com.au*

Kookaburra Backpackers

264 Charles St, Pialba
Hervey Bay QLD 4655

Phone   (07) 4124-2869
Fax   (07) 4124-2869
Freecall 1800-111-442
E-mail   *kookaburrabackpackers@yahoo.com*
Internet *www.kookaburrabackpackers.com*

Friendly Hostel

182 Torquay Rd, Scarness
Hervey Bay QLD 4655

Phone   (07) 4124-4107
Fax   (07) 4124-4619
Freecall 1800-244-107
E-mail   *friendlyhostel@bigpond.com*

Central Queensland

Central Queensland has traditionally consisted of working-class towns, and not much has changed - you won't find a lot of touristy attractions here, only the real country experience. Bundaberg is the first main stop, and it's also the beginning of the Great Barrier Reef so diving courses are plentiful. Much further north is Rockhampton, the next major city and gateway to popular Great Keppel Island. In-between, there's plenty of country-style adventure to be found...

Myella Farmstay

Myella
Baralaba QLD 4702

Phone   (07) 4998-1290
Fax   (07) 4998-1104
E-mail   *myella@bigpond.com*
Internet *www.myella.com*

Kroombit Tourist Park YHA

'Lochenbar', Valentine Plains
Biloela QLD 4715

Phone   (07) 4992-2186
Fax   (07) 4992-4186
E-mail   *lochenbar@kroombit.com.au*
Internet *www.kroombit.com.au*

Kellys Beach Resort YHA

6 Trevors Rd, Bargara
Bundaberg QLD 4670

Phone   (07) 4154-7200
Fax   (07) 4154-7300
Freecall 1800-246-141
E-mail   *perfectholiday@kellysbeachresort.com.au*
Internet *www.kellysbeachresort.com.au*

Dive Inn
66 Targo St
Bundaberg QLD 4670

Phone   (07) 4153-5761
Fax   (07) 4151-2110
Freecall 1800-068-167
E-mail   *julian@aquascuba.com.au*
Internet *www.aquascuba.com.au*

Emu Park Beach House

88 Pattison St
Emu Park QLD 4710

Phone   (07) 4939-6111
Fax   (07) 4938-7036
Freecall 1800-333-349
E-mail   *emu_house31@hotmail.com*

Iluka Forest Retreat

127 Logan Rd
Innes Park QLD 4670

Phone   (07) 4159-3230
E-mail   *iluka@ecotravellercentral.info*

Ascot Backpackers

117 Musgrave St
Rockhampton QLD 4700

Phone   (07) 4922-4719
Fax   (07) 4922-1076
E-mail   *info@ascothotel.com.au*
Internet *www.ascothotel.com.au*

Southside Holiday Village

Lower Dawson Rd, Highway 1
Rockhampton QLD 4700

Phone   (07) 4927-3013
Fax   (07) 4927-7750
Freecall 1800-075-911
E-mail *bookings@sshv.com.au*
Internet *www.sshv.com.au*

Cool Bananas Backpacker Lodge

2 Springs Rd
Town of 1770 QLD 4677

Phone   (07) 4974-7660
Fax   (07) 4974-7661
Freecall 1800-227-660
E-mail *wheeler_danny@hotmail.com*
Internet *www.coolbananas.biz.com*

1770 Backpackers

6 Captain Cook Drive
Town of 1770 QLD 4677

Phone   (07) 4974-9849
Freecall 1800-12-1770
E-mail *1770@bigpond.com*

Airlie Beach

Airlie Beach is most backpacker's idea of Paradise. The blue sky, sunshine, adventure activities, diving and sailing, parties, it's all here. Airlie Beach provides access to the Whitsunday Islands, and there are a very large number of different boating options available, ranging from cheap snorkelling jet-boat trips lasting 1 day to multi-day adventures on sailboats. The Great Barrier Reef here is very accessible so snorkelling and diving provide incredible underwater sceneries of colorful fish and coral. Day trips are also available to the upper-class resorts on the islands, allowing you to live like the rich and famous, even if it's just for a day!

Airlie Waterfront Backpackers

6 The Esplanade
Airlie Beach QLD 4802

Phone   (07) 4948-1300
Fax   (07) 4948-1311
Freecall 1800-089-000
E-mail   *info@airliebackpackers.com.au*
Internet *www.airliebackpackers.com.au*

Reefo's Backpackers Resort

147 Shute Harbour Rd
Airlie Beach QLD 4802

Phone   (07) 4946-6137
Fax   (07) 4946-6846
Freecall 1800-800-795
E-mail   *res@reeforesort.com*
Internet *www.reeforesort.com*

Backpackers by the Bay

12 Hermitage Drive
Airlie Beach QLD 4802

Phone   (07) 4646-7267
Fax   (07) 4646-7267
Freecall 1800-646-994
E-mail   *bythebay@whitsunday.net.au*
Internet *www.backpackersbythebay.com*

Beaches Backpackers

356 Shute Harbour Rd
Airlie Beach QLD 4802

Phone   (07) 4646-6244
Fax   (07) 4646-7764
Freecall 1800-636-630
E-mail   *airliebeach@beaches.com.au*
Internet *www.beaches.com.au*

Club Whitsunday

346 Shute Harbour Rd
Airlie Beach QLD 4802

Phone   (07) 4946-6182
Fax   (07) 4649-6890
Freecall 1800-678-755
E-mail   *mollo2@tpgi.com.au*
Internet *www.clubwhitsunday.com*

Koala Beach Resort

336 Shute Harbour Rd
Airlie Beach QLD 4802

Phone   (07) 4946-6001
Fax   (07) 4946-6761
Freecall 1800-466-444
E-mail   *backpackers-info@koalaresort.com.au*
Internet *www.koala-backpackers.com*

Magnums Whitsunday Village Resort

366-374 Shute Harbour Rd
Airlie Beach QLD 4802

Phone   (07) 4946-6266
Freecall 1800-624-634
E-mail   *info@magnums.com.au*
Internet *www.magnums.com.au*

Hook Island Resort

Hook Island
Proserpine QLD 4800

Phone   (07) 4946-9380
E-mail   *resort@hookis.com.au*
Internet *www.hookislandresort.com.au*

Townsville

There's something about Townsville that's different to the other cities north and south of here, and you can really feel a difference as soon as you arrive. It feels welcoming, perhaps it's the impressive scenery, the tropical weather, or the amazing Strand which has been built to provide a variety of swimming, relaxation and entertainment along the waterfront. Townsville has more sunny days per year than anywhere else in Queensland. It's also the gateway to nearby Magnetic Island which is so close it can be seen just off-shore.

Adventurers Backpackers

79 Palmer St
Townsville QLD 4810

Phone   (07) 4721-1522
Fax   (07) 4021-3251
Freecall 1800-211-522
E-mail *backpackers@adventurersresort.com*
Internet *www.adventurersresort.com*

Civic Guest House VIP

262 Walker St
Townsville QLD 4810

Phone   (07) 4771-5381
Fax   (07) 4721-4919
Freecall 1800-646-619
E-mail *civichouse@austarnet.com.au*
Internet *www.backpackersinn.com.au*

Southbank Village Backpackers

35 McIlwraith St
Townsville QLD 4810

Phone   (07) 4771-5849
E-mail   *southbank_village@bigpond.com*

Transit Centre Backpackers YHA

Corner Palmer & Plume Sts
Townsville South QLD 4810

Phone   (07) 4721-2322
Fax   (07) 4721-4044
E-mail   *info@tcbackpacker.com.au*
Internet *www.tcbackpacker.com.au*

Globetrotters Backpackers Hostel

45 Palmer St
Townsville South QLD 4810

Phone   (07) 4771-3242
Fax   (07) 4721-6402
E-mail   *globetrotters@austarnet.com.au*

Magnetic Island

Magnetic Island, or 'Maggie' as it's known to the locals, is just 20 minutes by ferry from Townsville. Two-thirds of the island is National Park, and there are plenty of secluded and beautiful beaches, as well as over 20km of walking tracks to be explored. Adventure activities and diving are also popular.

Arkies Resort

7 Marine Parade
Magnetic Island QLD 4819

Phone   (07) 4778-5177
Fax   (07) 4778-5939
Freecall 1800-663-666
E-mail *arkies_magnetic@bigpond.com.au*
Internet *www.arkiesonmagnetic.com*

Coconuts Backpackers

1 Nelly Bay Rd
Magnetic Island QLD 4819

Phone   (07) 4778-5777
Fax   (07) 4778-5507
Freecall 1800-065-696
E-mail *infococonuts@bakpakgroup.com*
Internet *www.bakpakgroup.com/coconuts*

Geoff's Place YHA

40 Horseshoe Bay Rd
Magnetic Island QLD 4819

Phone   (07) 4778-5577
Fax   (07) 4778-5781
Freecall 1800-285-577

E-mail   *geoffsplace@beyond.net.au*
Internet *www.geoffsplace.com.au*

Maggies Beach House

1 Pacific Drive, Horseshoe Bay
Magnetic Island QLD 4819

Phone   (07) 4778-5144
Fax   (07) 4778-5194
Freecall 1800-001-544
E-mail   *info@maggiesbeachhouse.com.au*
Internet *www.maggiesbeachhouse.com.au*

Magnetic Island Tropical Resort

56 Yates St, Nelly Bay
Magnetic Island QLD 4819

Phone   (07) 4778-5955
Fax   (07) 4778-5601
Freecall 1800-069-122
E-mail   *info@magnetictropicalresort.com*
Internet *www.magnetictropicalresort.com*

Travellers Backpackers Resort

1 The Esplanade, Picnic Bay
Magnetic Island QLD 4819

Phone   (07) 4778-5166
Fax   (07) 4758-1025
Freecall 1800-000-290
E-mail   *travellers@getonit.net.au*
Internet *www.travellers-on-maggie.com*

Centaur Guest House

27 Marine Parade, Arcadia
Magnetic Island QLD 4819

Phone   (07) 4778-5668
Fax   (07) 4778-5668
Freecall 1800-655-680
E-mail   *centaurhouse@hotkey.net.au*
Internet *www.hotkey.net.au/~centaurhouse*

Mission Beach

Mission Beach has a very laid-back atmosphere, in fact it may appear that everyone is just sitting around relaxing, with nowhere to go. Sure, there are activities available, rafting and bushwalking and horse riding and much more, but... it seems Mission Beach was made for simply hanging out. Maybe that's due to it's hippy past. This area is also one of the very few places where you may come across a Cassowary, a giant flightless bird with a colorful and unusual-looking horned head. It's a sight you'll remember, but don't get too close because they don't really like humans!

Mission Beach Backpackers Lodge

28 Wongaling Beach Rd
Mission Beach QLD 4852

Phone   (07) 4068-8317
Fax   (07) 4068-8616
Freecall 1800-688-316
E-mail   *mblodge@znet.net.au*
Internet *www.missionbeachbackpacker.com*

Mission Beach Resort

Wongaling Beach Rd
Mission Beach QLD 4852

Phone   (07) 4068-8288
Fax   (07) 4068-8429
Freecall 1800-079-024
E-mail   *mbr@znet.net.au*
Internet *www.missionbeachresort.com*

Mission Beach Retreat

49 Porter Promanade
Mission Beach QLD 4852

Phone   (07) 4088 6229
Fax   (07) 4088 6111
Freecall 1800-001-056
E-mail   *stay@missionbeachretreat.com.au*
Internet *www.missionbeachretreat.com.au*

Beach Shack

86 Porters Promenade
Mission Beach QLD 4852

Phone   (07) 4068-7783
Freecall 1800-333-115
E-mail   *beachshack_mb@bigpond.com*
Internet *www.missionbeachshack.com*

Scotty's Beach House

167 Reid Rd
Mission Beach QLD 4852

Phone   (07) 4068-8676
Fax   (07) 4068-8520
Freecall 1800-665-567
E-mail   *scottys@znet.net.au*
Internet *www.scottysbeachhouse.com.au*

Treehouse YHA

Bingil Bay Rd
Mission Beach QLD 4852

Phone   (07) 4068-7137
Fax   (07) 4068-7028
E-mail   *treehouse.yha@znet.net.au*
Internet *www.yha.org.au*

Bingil Bay Resort

The Esplanade / Cutten St
Bingil Bay QLD 4852

Phone   (07) 4068-7208
Fax   (07) 4068-7226
E-mail   *bingilbayresort@bigpond.com*

Sanctuary Retreat

Holts Rd
Bingil Bay QLD 4852

Phone   (07) 4088-6064
Fax   (07) 4088-6071
Freecall 1800-777-012
E-mail   *seek@sanctuaryatmission.com*
Internet *www.sanctuaryatmission.com*

Cairns

Cairns is near the top of Far North Queensland and for many travelers it's the farthest they'll be going. Perhaps that's why there's non-stop parties here, and it seems that Cairns is determined to provide more party per square meter than any other city in Australia. Apart from the nightlife and entertainment, there's also an abundance of adventure activities such as sky diving, sea kayaking, whitewater rafting, bungy jumping, and all the regular not-quite-so-extreme activities too... Think of any activity and yes, it's probably here.

Utopia Cairns

702 Bruce Highway
Cairns QLD 4868

Phone   (07) 4054-4444
Fax   (07) 4033-1016
Freecall 1800-354-599
E-mail   *utopia01@ozemail.com.au*
Internet *www.nomadsutopiacairns.com.au*

Captain Cook Backpackers Resort

204-212 Sheridan St
Cairns QLD 4870

Phone   (07) 4051-6811
Fax   (07) 4051-7507
Freecall 1800-243-512
E-mail   *inquiries@backpacker-cairns.com*
Internet *www.backpacker-cairns.com*

Bohemia Resort

231 McLeod St
Cairns QLD 4870

Phone   (07) 4041-7290
Fax   (07) 4041-7292
Freecall 1800-155-353
E-mail   *info@bohemiaresort.com.au*
Internet *www.bohemiaresort.com.au*

Cairns Holiday Lodge

259 Sheridan St
Cairns QLD 4870

Phone   (07) 4051-4611
Fax   (07) 4051-1926
Freecall 1800-224-764
E-mail   *reservations@cairnsholidaylodge.com.au*
Internet *www.cairnsholidaylodge.com.au*

Calypso Inn Backpackers Resort

5-9 Digger St
Cairns QLD 4870

Phone   (07) 4031-0910
Fax   (07) 4051-7518
Freecall 1800-815-628
E-mail   *admin@calypsobackpackers.com.au*
Internet *www.calypsobackpackers.com.au*

Caravella 77 Backpackers

77 The Esplanade
Cairns QLD 4870

Phone   (07) 4051-2431
Fax   (07) 4031-6329
Freecall 1800-814-019
E-mail   *info@caravella.com.au*
Internet *www.caravella.com.au*

Castaways Backpackers

207 Sheridan St
Cairns QLD 4870

Phone   (07) 4051-1238
Fax   (07) 4052-1804
Freecall 1800-351-115
E-mail   *castaways@castawaysbackpackers.com.au*
Internet *www.castawaysbackpackers.com.au*

Gecko's Backpackers

187 Bunda St
Cairns QLD 4870

Phone   (07) 4031-1344
Fax   (07) 4051-5150
Freecall 1800-011-344
E-mail   *bookings@geckosbackpackers.com.au*
Internet *www.geckosbackpackers.com.au*

Inn the Tropics

141 Sheridan St
Cairns QLD 4870

Phone   (07) 4031-1088
Fax   (07) 4051-7110
Freecall 1800-807-055
E-mail   *innthetropics@cairns.net.au*
Internet *www.innthetropics.com*

The International Hostel

67-69 The Esplanade
Cairns QLD 4870

Phone   (07) 4031-1545
Fax   (07) 4031-3804
Freecall 1800-682-647
E-mail   *info@internationalhostel.com.au*
Internet *www.internationalhostel.com.au*

Koala Beach Resort

137-139 Lake St
Cairns QLD 4870

Phone   (07) 4051-4933
Fax   (07) 4051-9716
Freecall 1800-466-444
E-mail   *backpackers-info@koalaresort.com.au*
Internet *www.koala-backpackers.com*

Pete's Cairns Backpacker Resort

242-248 Grafton St
Cairns QLD 4870

Phone   (07) 4031-6938
Fax   (07) 4031-4872
Freecall 1800-122-123
E-mail   *info@petescairns.com.au*
Internet *www.petescairns.com.au*

Serpent Hostel & Bar

341 Lake St
Cairns QLD 4870

Phone   (07) 4040-7777
Fax   (07) 4031-8401
Freecall 1800-737-736
E-mail   *info@serpenthostel.com*
Internet *www.serpenthostel.com*

Cairns Central YHA

20-24 McLeod St
Cairns QLD 4870

Phone   (07) 4051-0772
Fax   (07) 4031-3158
E-mail   *cairnscentral@yhaqld.org*
Internet *www.yha.org.au*

YHA On The Esplanade

93 The Esplanade
Cairns QLD 4870

Phone   (07) 4031-1919
Fax   (07) 4031-4381
E-mail   *cairnsesplanade@yhaqld.org*
Internet *www.yha.org.au*

Leo's Backpackers

100 Sheridan St
Cairns QLD 4870

Phone   (07) 4051-1264
Fax   (07) 4031-6281
Freecall 1800-080-809
E-mail   *leos@explore-oz.com*

Rosie's International Backpackers

136 Grafton St
Cairns QLD 4870

Phone   (07) 4041-0249
Fax   (07) 4041-0252
Freecall 1800-152-000
E-mail   *rosiesbackpackers@hotmail.com*

Bel-Air by the Sea

155-157 The Esplanade
Cairns QLD 4870

Phone   (07) 4031-4790
Fax   (07) 4052-1972
Freecall 1800-649-517
E-mail   *belair@cairns.net.au*
Internet *www.cairns.net.au/~haka*

Cairns Girls Hostel

147 Lake St
Cairns QLD 4870

Phone   (07) 4051-2016
Fax   (07) 4051-2016
Freecall 1800-011-950
E-mail   *cairnsgirlshostel@bigpond.com.au*
Internet *www.cairnsgirlshostel.com.au*

Dreamtime

4 Terminus St
Cairns QLD 4870

Phone   (07) 4031-6753
Fax   (07) 4031-6566
E-mail   *dreamtime@dreamtimetravel.com.au*
Internet *www.dreamtimetravel.com.au/dt*

Inn the City

141 Lake St
Cairns QLD 4870

Phone   (07) 4051-3633
E-mail   *res@inn-the-city.com*
Internet *www.inn-the-city.com*

Travellers Oasis

8 Scott St
Cairns QLD 4870

Phone   (07) 4052-1377
Fax   (07) 4041-7456
Freecall 1800-621-353
E-mail   *travoasis@travoasis.com.au*
Internet *www.travoasis.com.au*

Asylum Backpackers

149 Grafton St
Cairns QLD 4876

Phone   (07) 4031-1474
Fax   (07) 4031-8499
Freecall 1800-065-464
E-mail   *cairnsbackpackers@cairns.net.au*
Internet *www.asylumbackpackers.com*

The Big Backyard

34 Martyn St
Cairns QLD 4876

Phone   (07) 4031-3133
Fax   (07) 4031-3150
Freecall 1800-025-070
E-mail   *info@backyard.com.au*
Internet *www.backyard.com.au*

Cairns Beachhouse

239 Sheridan St
Cairns QLD 4876

Phone   (07) 4041-4116
Fax   (07) 4041-0431
Freecall 1800-229-228
E-mail   *talk2us@cairnsbeachhouse.com.au*
Internet *www.cairnsbeachhouse.com.au*

Club Croc Hides Hotel

87 Lake St
Cairns QLD 4876

Phone   (07) 4051-1266
Fax   (07) 4031-2276
Freecall 1800-079-266
E-mail   *hideshotel@clubcroc.com.au*
Internet *www.clubcroc.com.au*

The Global Palace

86 Lake St
Cairns QLD 4876

Phone   (07) 4031-7921
Fax   (07) 4031-3231
Freecall 1800-819-024
E-mail   *info@globalpalace.com.au*
Internet *www.globalpalace.com.au*

Tropic Days

28 Bunting St
Cairns QLD 4876

Phone   (07) 4041-1521
Fax   (07) 4031-6576
E-mail   *info@tropicdays.com.au*
Internet *www.tropicdays.com.au*

Up Top Down Under

164-170 Spence St
Cairns QLD 4876

Phone   (07) 4051-3636
Freecall 1800-243-944
E-mail   *uptop@uptopdownunder.com.au*
Internet *www.uptopdownunder.com.au*

Far North Queensland

Far North Queensland is a vast area with many attractions, beginning in Townsville, up to Cairns and going just a little further up the coast, also extending inland. Bowen and Cardwell are very popular spots for finding harvest work, the Daintree and Kuranda offer incomparable rainforest experiences, and the Undara Lava Tubes are an absolutely unforgettable experience, although they can only be seen as part of guided tours which are a little above the usual backpacker prices - but well worth it. Port Douglas is just north of Cairns and is a popular up-market holiday spot, offering a more laid-back atmosphere than Cairns and with some great beaches. At the very top is Cape Tribulation, the farthest north you can go without a 4-wheel drive - and the scenery here is unmissable.

Atherton Backpackers

37 Alice St
Atherton QLD 4883

Phone   (07) 4091-3552
E-mail   *athertonbackpack@hotmail.com*

Bogie River Bush House

Normanby Rd
Bowen QLD 4805

Phone   (07) 4785-3407
Fax   (07) 4785-3321
E-mail   *bogierbh@tpg.com.au*
Internet *www.bogiebushhouse.com.au*

Bowen Backpackers

Corner Herbert & Dalrymple Sts
Bowen QLD 4805

Phone   (07) 4786-3433
E-mail   *bowenbackpackers@bigpond.com*
Internet *www.users.bigpond.com/bowenbackpackers*

Cape Trib Beach House

Cape Tribulation Rd
Cape Tribulation QLD 4873

Phone   (07) 4098-0030
Fax   (07) 4098-0120
Freecall 1800-111-124
E-mail   *reservations@capetribbeach.com.au*
Internet *www.capetribbeach.com.au*

Crocodylus Village YHA

Buchanan Creek Rd, Cow Bay
Cape Tribulation QLD 4873

Phone   (07) 4098-9166
Fax   (07) 4098-9131
E-mail   *info@crocodyluscapetrib.com*
Internet *www.crocodyluscapetrib.com*

PK's Jungle Village

Cape Tribulation Rd
Cape Tribulation QLD 4873

Phone   (07) 4098-0040
Fax   (07) 4098-0055
Freecall 1800-232-333
E-mail   *info@pksjunglevillage.com*
Internet *www.pksjunglevillage.com.au*

Hinchinbrook YHA

175 Bruce Highway
Cardwell QLD 4849

Phone   (07) 4066-8648
Fax   (07) 4066-8910
E-mail   *kookaburra@znet.net.au*
Internet *www.kookaburraholidaypark.com.au*

Cardwell Backpackers Hostel

178 Bowen St
Cardwell QLD 4849

Phone   (07) 4066-8014
Fax   (07) 4066-8014
E-mail   *cardwellbackpackers@bigpond.com*

Mount Mulligan Farmstay

Mount Mulligan Rd
Chillagoe QLD 4871

Phone   (07) 4094-8360
Freecall 1800-359-798
E-mail   *mount_mulligan@bigpond.com*

Pam's Place YHA

Corner Charlotte & Boundary Sts
Cooktown QLD 4871

Phone   (07) 4069-5166
Fax   (07) 4069-5964
E-mail   *pamplace@tpg.com.au*
Internet *www.cooktownhostel.com*

Koala Beach Resort

Cape Kimberly Rd
Daintree QLD 4802

Phone   (07) 4090-7500
Fax   (07) 4090-7501
Freecall 1800-466-444
E-mail   *backpackers-info@koalaresort.com.au*
Internet *www.koala-backpackers.com*

Walkabout Motel

20 McGowan Drive
Innisfail QLD 4860

Phone   (07) 4061-2311
Fax   (07) 4061-4919
E-mail   *motelwalkabout@bigpond.com*

Kuranda Backpackers Hostel

6 Arara St
Kuranda QLD 4872

Phone   (07) 4093-7355
Fax   (07) 4093-7295
E-mail   *info@kurandabackpackershostel.com*
Internet *www.kurandabackpackershostel.com*

Kuranda Rainforest Park

Kuranda Heights Rd
Kuranda QLD 4872

Phone   (07) 4093-7316
Fax   (07) 4093-7316
E-mail   *info@kurandatouristpark.com*
Internet *www.kurandatouristpark.com*

Larrikin Lodge YHA

32 Peel St
Mackay QLD 4740

Phone   (07) 4951-3728
Fax   (07) 4957-2978

E-mail *larrikin@mackay.net.au*
Internet *www.yha.org.au*

Travellers Haven

Corner Spence & Pamela Sts
Mount Isa QLD 4825

Phone   (07) 4743-0313
Fax   (07) 4743-4007
E-mail *thehaven@bigpond.net.au*
Internet *www.users.bigpond.net.au/travellershaven*

Undara Lava Lodge YHA

Undara
Mt Surprise QLD 4870

Phone   (07) 4097-1411
Fax   (07) 4097-1450
Freecall 1800-990-992
E-mail *res@undara.com.au*
Internet *www.undara.com.au*

Dougies Backpackers Resort

111 Davidson St
Port Douglas QLD 4871

Phone   (07) 4099-6200
Fax   (07) 4099-6047
Freecall 1800-996-200
E-mail *info@dougies.com.au*
Internet *www.dougies.com.au*

Parrotfish Lodge

37-39 Warner St
Port Douglas QLD 4871

Phone   (07) 4099-5011
Fax   (07) 4099-5044
Freecall 1800-995-011
E-mail *info@parrotfishlodge.com*
Internet *www.parrotfishlodge.com*

Port O'Call Lodge YHA

Port St
Port Douglas QLD 4871

Phone   (07) 4099-5422
Fax   (07) 4099-5495
Freecall 1800-892-800
E-mail *info@portocall.com.au*
Internet *www.portocall.com.au*

South Australia (SA)

South Australia is a vast state, largely unexplored by backpackers, with the exception of the capital Adelaide. Adelaide seems to always have a large backpacker population experiencing the fine culture, arts and food. Nearby Glenelg offers beaches and water sports.

Kangaroo Island is also very popular with travelers - and even more popular with the animals there! The island has no natural predators, so the island's large population of koalas, kangaroos, lizards, birds, seals and more are all very easy to find.

Coober Pedy is a unique and unusual town where thousands of people live under the ground to escape the heat. Due to the scenery here being so unusual, this area was used for filming parts of Mad Max, Pitch Black, and other movies, and it's worth a look. Outback South Australia not only offers the true country experience, many places are also popular locations to find backpacker work.

Adelaide

Adelaide, the capital of South Australia, is a place of culture, refinement and history. Museums, festivals, parks, and the river Torrens are all attractions, and this quieter atmosphere does satisfy the needs of many backpackers, along with ample food and wine, and nightlife. Nearby Glenelg is only 10km from the city and has beaches, windsurfing, great restaurants and is definitely worth a visit. Adelaide also acts as the gateway to many other popular regions such as Kangaroo Island and Coober Pedy, as well being an ideal stop-over point on the way to/from Alice Springs in the Northern Territory or Perth in Western Australia.

Adelaide Travellers Inn

118 Carrington St
Adelaide SA 5000

Phone   (08) 8224-0753
Freecall 1800-633-747
E-mail   *intravel@senet.com.au*
Internet *www.adelaidebackpackers.com.au*

Adelaide Backpackers Hostel

257 Waymouth St
Adelaide SA 5000

Phone   (08) 8221-5299
Fax   (08) 8221-5244
Freecall 1800-221-529
E-mail   *bookings@adelaidehostel.com.au*
Internet *www.adelaidehostel.com.au*

Nomads Tatts

17 Hindley St
Adelaide SA 5000

Phone   (08) 8231-3225
Fax   (08) 8410-2929
Freecall 1800-133-355
E-mail   *tattscity@hotmail.com*
Internet *www.backpackersadelaide.com*

BackPack Oz

144 Wakefield St
Adelaide SA 5000

Phone   (08) 8223-3551
Fax   (08) 8223-3551
Freecall 1800-633-307
E-mail   *enquiries@backpackoz.com.au*
Internet *www.backpackoz.com.au*

Blue Galah Backpackers Hostel

62 King William St
Adelaide SA 5000

Phone   (08) 8231-9295
Fax   (08) 8231-9258
Freecall 1800-555-322
E-mail   *info@bluegalah.com.au*
Internet *www.bluegalah.com.au*

Brecon Inn

11-13 Gilbert St
Adelaide SA 5000

Phone   (08) 8211-8985
Fax   (08) 8211-8748
Freecall 1800-990-009
E-mail *enquiries@breconinn.com.au*
Internet *www.breconinn.com.au*

East Park Lodge

341 Angus St
Adelaide SA 5000

Phone   (08) 8223-1228
Fax   (08) 8223-7772
Freecall 1800-643-606
E-mail *stay@eastparklodge.com.au*
Internet *www.eastparklodge.com.au*

Cannon St Backpackers

11 Cannon St
Adelaide SA 5000

Phone   (08) 8410-1218
Fax   (08) 8410-1218
Freecall 1800-069-731
E-mail *cannonst@senet.com.au*
Internet *www.senet.com.au/cannonst*

Sunny's Backpackers Hostel

139 Franklin St
Adelaide SA 5000

Phone   (08) 8231-2430
Fax   (08) 8231-0131
Freecall 1800-786-697
E-mail   *beds@adelaidebackpackers.com*
Internet *www.sunnys.com.au*

Adelaide Backpackers Inn

112 Carrington St
Adelaide SA 5000

Phone   (08) 8223-3866
Fax   (08) 8232-5464
Freecall 1800-247-725
E-mail   *abackinn@tne.net.au*
Internet *www.tne.net.au/abackinn*

Adelaide Central YHA

135 Waymouth St
Adelaide SA 5000

Phone   (08) 8410-3010
Fax   (08) 8414-3015
Freecall 1800-222-942
E-mail   *adlcentral@yhasa.org.au*
Internet *www.yha.org.au*

Geoff & Hazel's Backpackers for Couples

19 Kingsland Rd
Aldgate SA 5154

Phone   (08) 8339-8360
E-mail   *geoffandhazels@picknowl.com.au*
Internet *www.geoffandhazels.com.au*

Glenelg Beach Resort

1-7 Mosely St
Glenelg SA 5045

Phone   (08) 8376-0007
Fax   (08) 8376-0007
Freecall 1800-066-422
E-mail   *info@glenelgbeachresort.com.au*
Internet *www.glenelgbeachresort.com.au*

Other Areas

Much of South Australia is a vast and dry state, and nowhere is this more apparent than in the outback town of Coober Pedy, where more than 4000 residents live under the ground to escape the desert heat! This makes for an interesting lifestyle and scenery, and it's also a major center for opal mining (you can have a go yourself), so it's a place not to be missed. Kangaroo Island, south of Adelaide, is also unique with an unbelievable abundance of wildlife, more than you would expect or imagine! Much of South Australia is off the usual backpacker route and is worth exploring for the true country experience.

Barmera Backpackers YHA

6 Bice St
Barmera SA 5345

Phone   (08) 8588-3007
Fax   (08) 8588-3035
E-mail   *backpack@riverland.net.au*
Internet *www.yha.org.au*

Cape Jervis Station

Cape Jervis Rd
Cape Jervis SA 5204

Phone   (08) 8598-0288
Fax   (08) 8598-0278
Freecall 1800-805-288
E-mail   *admin@capejervisstation.com.au*
Internet *www.capejervisstation.com.au*

Ceduna Shelly Beach Caravan Park

178 Decres Rd
Ceduna SA 5690

Phone   (08) 8625-2012
Fax   (08) 8625-2012
E-mail   *shellycp@tpg.com.au*
Internet *www.cedunacaravanpark.com.au*

Opal Inn

Hutchison St
Coober Pedy SA 5723

Phone   (08) 8672-5054
Fax   (08) 8672-5501
Freecall 1800-088-523
E-mail   *reservations@opalinn.com.au*
Internet *www.opalinn.com.au*

Radeka's Downunder Backpackers

1 Oliver St
Coober Pedy SA 5723

Phone   (08) 8672-5223
Fax   (08) 8672-5821
Freecall 1800-633-891
E-mail   *radekadownunder@ozemail.com.au*
Internet *www.radekadownunder.com.au*

Kangaroo Island YHA

33 Middle Terrace
Kangaroo Island SA 5222

Phone   (08) 8553-1344
Fax   (08) 8553-1344
Freecall 1800-018-484
E-mail   *yha@ki-ferryconnections.com*
Internet *www.ki-ferryconnections.com*

Penneshaw Youth Hostel

43 North Terrace, Penneshaw
Kangaroo Island SA 5222

Phone   (08) 8553-1284
Fax   (08) 8553-1295
Freecall 1800-686-620
E-mail   *advhost@bigpond.com*
Internet *www.penneshawyh.com*

Nomads on Murray

Sturt Highway
Kingston on Murray SA 5331

Phone   (08) 8583-0211
Fax   (08) 8583-0206
Freecall 1800-665-166
E-mail   *mobconsultancy@bigpond.com*
Internet *www.nomadsworld.com/oz*

Harvest Trail Lodge

1 Kokoda Terrace
Loxton SA 5333

Phone   (08) 8584-5646
Fax   (08) 8584-5630
E-mail   *lodge@dodo.com.au*
Internet *www.harvesttrail.com*

The Jail YHA

25 Margaret St
Mount Gambier SA 5290

Phone   (08) 8723-0032
Fax   (08) 8723-2477
Freecall 1800-626-844
E-mail   *turnkey@seol.net.au*
Internet *www.jailbackpackers.com*

Murray Bridge Backpackers

1 McKay Rd
Murray Bridge SA 5253

Phone   (08) 8532-6994
Fax   (08) 8531-3400
E-mail   *john@mbbackpackershostel.com.au*
Internet *www.mbbackpackershostel.com.au*

Naracoorte Backpackers YHA

4 Jones St
Naracoorte SA 5271

Phone   (08) 8762-3835
Fax   (08) 8762-3835
E-mail   *sonja@rbm.com.au*
Internet *www.yha.org.au*

Parachilna Overflow

Corner High St & West Terrace
Parachilna SA 5730

Phone   (08) 8648-4844
Fax   (08) 8648-4606
E-mail   *info@prairiehotel.com.au*
Internet *www.prairiehotel.com.au*

Backpackers Travellers Hostel

86-90 Railway Terrace
Peterborough SA 5422

Phone   (08) 8651-2711
E-mail   *contacts@travellersoz.com.au*
Internet *www.travellersoz.com*

Blue Fox Lodge

Corner Trent Rd & National Highway One
Port Augusta SA 5700

Phone   (08) 8641-2960
E-mail   *bluefoxlodge@ozzienet.net*
Internet *www.bluefoxlodge.com*

Arnella by the Sea YHA

28 North Terrace
Port Elliot SA 5212

Phone   (08) 8554-3611
Fax   (08) 8554-3177
Freecall 1800-066-297
E-mail   *narnu@bigpond.com*
Internet *www.yha.org.au*

Flinders Ranges Andu Lodge YHA

12 First St
Quorn SA 5433

Phone   (08) 8648-6655
Fax   (08) 8648-6898
Freecall 1800-639-933
E-mail   *info@headingbush.com*
Internet *www.headingbush.com*

Robe Long Beach Holiday Park YHA

70-80 The Esplanade
Robe SA 5276

Phone   (08) 8768-2237
Fax   (08) 8768-2730
E-mail   *robelongbeachpark@bigpond.com*
Internet *www.robelongbeach.com.au*

Mt Lofty Railway Station Lodge

2 Sturt Valley Rd
Stirling SA 5152

Phone   (08) 8339-7400
Fax   (08) 8339-5560
E-mail   *lodge@mlrs.com.au*
Internet *www.mlrs.com.au*

Sea Breeze Hotel

7 Tumby Terrace
Tumby Bay SA 5605

Phone   (08) 8688-2362
Fax   (08) 8688-2722
E-mail   *seabreeze1@ozemail.com.au*
Internet *www.tumbybay.aust.com/seabrez.htm*

Grosvenor Hotel

40 Ocean St
Victor Harbor SA 5211

Phone   (08) 8552-1011
Fax   (08) 8552-7274
E-mail   *grosvenr@granite.net.au*

Mount Dutton Bay Woolshed

Off Flinders Highway
Wangary SA 5607

Phone   (08) 8685-4031
Fax   (08) 8685-4031
E-mail   *woolshed@duttonbay.com*
Internet *www.duttonbay.com*

Woomera Travellers Village

Old Pimba Rd
Woomera SA 5720

Phone   (08) 8673-7800
Fax   (08) 8673-7700
E-mail   *info@woomera.com*
Internet *www.woomera.com*

Tasmania (TAS)

Tasmania is Australia's best kept secret, and most backpackers don't make it this far south but those who do never regret it. 'Tassie' is Australia's only island state, and it's easily reached by either a quick flight to Hobart or Launceston, or the popular overnight ferry from Melbourne to the small city of Devonport. If you're a lover of nature and want to experience a vast wilderness then the countryside of Tasmania is a must-see, with some of the most scenic National Park walks in the world located here.

Hobart

Hobart is Tasmania's capital and is Australia's 2nd oldest city, yet only has a population of around 200,000. Hobart's waterfront area is the center of entertainment, markets, and cool places to hang out. The Cascade Brewery also offers a very popular tour for beer fans. Many of Hobart's historic sandstone buildings have been preserved and provide an interesting perspective on early Australian architecture.

Central City Backpackers

138 Collins St
Hobart TAS 7000

Phone   (03) 6224-2404
Fax   (03) 6224-2404
Freecall 1800-811-507
E-mail   *bookings@centralbackpackers.com.au*
Internet *www.centralbackpackers.com.au*

Transit Centre Backpackers

1st Floor Transit Centre, 199 Collins St
Hobart TAS 7000

Phone   (03) 6231-2400
Fax   (03) 6231-2400
E-mail   *lizk@southcom.com.au*
Internet *www.salamanca.com.au/backpackers*

Ocean Child Hotel

86 Argyle St
Hobart TAS 7000

Phone   (03) 6234-6730
Fax   (03) 6234-9306
E-mail   *oceanchild@sullivanscove.com*
Internet *www.sullivanscove.com/oceanchild*

Pickled Frog Backpackers

281 Liverpool St
Hobart TAS 7000

Phone   (03) 6234-7977
Fax   (03) 6234-4628
E-mail   *info@thepickledfrog.com*
Internet *www.thepickledfrog.com*

Montgomery's YHA Backpackers

9 Argyle St
Hobart TAS 7000

Phone   (03) 6231-2660
Fax   (03) 6231-4817
E-mail   *montys@southcom.com.au*
Internet *www.yha.org.au*

Allport's Hostel

432 Elizabeth St
Hobart North TAS 7000

Phone   (03) 6231-5464
E-mail   *allports@tassie.net.au*
Internet *www.tassie.net.au/~allports*

Waterfront Cottage

153 Risdon Rd
Newtown Bay TAS 7008

Phone   (03) 6228-4748
Fax   (03) 6228-1945
E-mail   *info@waterfrontnewtownbay.com*
Internet *www.waterfrontnewtownbay.com*

Launceston

Launceston is Tasmania's 2nd largest city and Australia's 3rd oldest. If you come to Tasmania by ferry then you'll arrive in Devonport on the north coast, which is not far from Launceston (much closer than Hobart in the South). Launceston offers travelers a variety of activities such as forest walks, wilderness tours, historic tours, and the very popular Cataract Gorge, a ravine with a rushing river and picturesque forest scenery.

Launceston City Youth Hostel

36 Thistle St
Launceston TAS 7250

Phone   (03) 6344-9779
Fax   (03) 6344-9779
E-mail   *tasequiphire@email.com*
Internet lcyh.fusionwave.net

Andy's No.1 Backpackers

Mallee Grill, 1 Tamar St
Launceston TAS 7250

Phone   (03) 6334-9288
Fax   (03) 6334-7953
E-mail   *andy@andys.com.au*
Internet *www.andys.com.au*

Metro Backpackers YHA

16 Brisbane St
Launceston TAS 7250

Phone   (03) 6334-4505
Fax   (03) 6334-8777
E-mail   *metrolaunceston@bigpond.com*
Internet *www.backpackersmetro.com.au*

Launceston Backpackers Hostel

103 Canning St
Launceston TAS 7250

Phone   (03) 6334-2327
Fax   (03) 6334-2624
E-mail   *wivells@bigpond.com*
Internet *www.launcestonbackpackers.com.au*

Other Areas

The countryside of Tasmania offers an absolutely massive range of unforgettable wilderness, National Parks, mountains, beaches, bays, forests, and friendly welcoming people.

Bridport Seaside Lodge Backpackers YHA

47 Main St
Bridport TAS 7262

Phone   (03) 6356-1585
Fax   (03) 6356-1585
E-mail   *seasidelodge@bigpond.com.au*
Internet *www.bridport.tco.asn.au/lodge*

Iluka Backpackers YHA

Esplanade
Coles Bay TAS 7215

Phone   (03) 6257-0115
Fax   (03) 6257-0384
Freecall 1800-786-512
E-mail   *ilukaholidaycentre@bigpond.com.au*
Internet *www.ilukaholidaycentre.com.au*

Cradle Mountain Backpackers YHA

Cradle Mountain Rd
Cradle Mountain TAS 7306

Phone   (03) 6492-1395
Fax   (03) 6492-1438
E-mail   *cradle@cosycabins.com*
Internet *www.cosycabins.com*

Balfes Hill Huon Valley Backpackers

4 Sandhill Rd
Cradoc TAS 7109

Phone   (03) 6295-1551
Fax   (03) 6295-0875
E-mail   *huonvalley@tassie.net.au*
Internet *www.balfeshill.alltasmanian.com*

Highview Lodge YHA

8 Blake St
Deloraine TAS 7304

Phone   (03) 6362-2996
E-mail   *bodach@microtech.com.au*
Internet *www.yha.org.au*

Formby Road Hostel

16 Formby Rd
Devonport TAS 7310

Phone   (03) 6423-6563
Fax   (03) 6428-7468
E-mail   *formbyrdhostel@ozemail.com.au*
Internet *www.devonport.tco.asn.au/formby*

Tasman House Backpackers

114 Tasman St
Devonport TAS 7310

Phone   (03) 6423-2335
Fax   (03) 6423-2340
E-mail   *tasmanhouse@vision.net.au*
Internet *www.tasmanhouse.com*

Geeveston Forest House

24 Arve Rd
Geeveston TAS 7116

Phone   (03) 6297-1102
E-mail   *lauriedillon@tassie.net.au*
Internet *www.tassie.net.au/~ldillon*

Travellers Lodge YHA

4 Elizabeth St
George Town TAS 7253

Phone   (03) 6382-3261
Fax   (03) 6382-3261
E-mail *travellerslodge_yha@hotmail.com*
Internet *www.yha.org.au*

Pelican Sands Backpackers

157 Scamander Avenue
Scamander TAS 7215

Phone   (03) 6372-5231
Fax   (03) 6372-5340
E-mail *info@pelicansandsscamander.com.au*
Internet *www.pelicansandsscamander.com.au*

Sheffield Backpackers

Corner of Henry & Main Sts
Sheffield TAS 7306

Phone   (03) 6491-2611
E-mail *enquiries@sheffieldbackpackers.com.au*
Internet *www.sheffieldbackpackers.com.au*

Seaview Farm Lodge

German Town Rd
St.Mary's TAS 7215

Phone   (03) 6372-2341
E-mail   *julia.seaview@tassie.net.au*
Internet *www.seaviewfarm.com.au*

Stanley YHA

Wharf Rd
Stanley TAS 7331

Phone   (03) 6458-1266
Fax   (03) 6458-1266
E-mail   *enquiries@stanleycabinpark.com.au*
Internet *www.yha.org.au*

Strahan YHA

43 Harvey St
Strahan TAS 7468

Phone   (03) 6471-7255
Fax   (03) 6471-7513
Freecall 1800-444-442
E-mail   *strahancentral@trump.net.au*
Internet *www.yha.org.au*

Triabunna YHA

12 Spencer St
Triabunna TAS 7190

Phone   (03) 6257-3439
Fax   (03) 6257-3439
E-mail   *udda@southcom.com.au*
Internet *www.yha.org.au*

Merlinkei Farm YHA

524 Racecourse Rd
Winnaleah TAS 7265

Phone   (03) 6354-2152
Fax   (03) 6354-1000
E-mail   *mervync@vision.net.au*
Internet *www.winnaleah.tco.asn.au/yha*

Victoria (VIC)

Victoria offers something for everyone. Melbourne claims the title of cultural capital of Australia, with cafes and food and shopping, and the suburbs are interesting with the grooviness of St Kilda and the up-market Prahran.

The Great Ocean Road is a highlight of Australia's natural scenery and no traveler should miss it. There's also incredible beauty in the mountains and National Parks in Victoria. In the south Phillip Island is worth visiting for the rare sight of watching the hundreds of fairy penguins as they come out of the ocean and return to their homes and children each night. There are also plenty of opportunities to find backpacker work in Victoria's countryside.

Melbourne - Central

Melbourne is the capital of Victoria, and also claims to be Australia's capital of arts and culture. Food, fashion, shopping, cafes, more shopping, more fashion, more food and more cafes. The parks and trams also add to the ambience. The nightlife is very social and there's something for everyone.

All Nations Backpackers Hotel

2 Spencer St
Melbourne VIC 3000

Phone   (03) 9620-1022
Fax   (03) 9620-1033
Freecall 1800-222-238
E-mail   *reservations@allnations.com.au*
Internet *www.allnations.com.au*

Hotel Bakpak

167 Franklin St
Melbourne VIC 3000

Phone   (03) 9329-7525
Fax   (03) 9326-7667
Freecall 1800-645-200
E-mail   *infofranklin@bakpakgroup.com*
Internet *www.bakpakgroup.com/franklin*

Elephant Backpackers

250 Flinders St
Melbourne VIC 3000

Phone   (03) 9654-2616
Fax   (03) 9663-7009
Freecall 1800-002-616
E-mail   *elephantb@hotmail.com*
Internet
www.elephantbackpackers.citysearch.com.au

Exford Hotel

199 Russell St
Melbourne VIC 3000

Phone   (03) 9663-2697
Fax   (03) 9663-2248
E-mail   *res@exfordhotel.com.au*
Internet *www.exfordhotel.com.au*

Flinders Station Hotel

35 Elizabeth St
Melbourne VIC 3000

Phone   (03) 9620-5100
Fax   (03) 9620-5101
E-mail   *res@flindersbackpackers.com.au*
Internet *www.flindersbackpackers.com.au*

The Friendly Backpacker

197 King St
Melbourne VIC 3000

Phone   (03) 9670-1111
Fax   (03) 9670-9911
Freecall 1800-671-115
E-mail   *friendly@friendlygroup.com.au*
Internet *www.friendlygroup.com.au*

The Greenhouse Backpacker

228 Flinders Lane
Melbourne VIC 3000

Phone   (03) 9639-6400
Fax   (03) 9639-6900
Freecall 1800-249-207
E-mail   *greenhouse@friendlygroup.com.au*
Internet *www.friendlygroup.com.au*

Melbourne Connection Travellers Hostel

205 King St
Melbourne VIC 3000

Phone   (03) 9642-4464
Fax   (03) 9642-0643
E-mail   *info@melbourneconnection.com*
Internet *www.melbourneconnection.com*

Melbourne International Backpackers

450 Elizabeth St
Melbourne VIC 3000

Phone   (03) 9662-4066
Fax   (03) 9662-4077
E-mail
res@melbourneinternationalbackpackers.com.au
Internet
www.melbourneinternationalbackpackers.com.au

Taylors on A'Beckett

106-112 A'Beckett St
Melbourne VIC 3000

Phone   (03) 9328-8449
Fax   (03) 9329-0199
E-mail   *info@toab.com.au*
Internet *www.toab.com.au*

Victoria Hall

380 Russell St
Melbourne VIC 3000

Phone   (03) 9662-3888
Fax   (03) 9639-0101
E-mail   *reception@victoriahall.com.au*
Internet *www.victoriahall.com.au*

Elizabeth Aus-Asia Hostel

Level 1, 490 Elizabeth St
Melbourne VIC 3000

Phone   (03) 9663-1685
Fax   (03) 9639-6719
E-mail   *elizabethhostel@hotmail.com*
Internet *www.elizabethhostel.citysearch.com.au*

Stork Hotel

504 Elizabeth St
Melbourne VIC 3000

Phone   (03) 9663-6237
Fax   (03) 9663-8895
E-mail   *admin@storkhotel.com*
Internet *www.storkhotel.com*

Toad Hall

441 Elizabeth St
Melbourne VIC 3000

Phone   (03) 9600-9010
Fax   (03) 9600-9013
E-mail   *toadhall.hotel@bigpond.com*
Internet *www.toadhall-hotel.com.au*

The Spencer - City Central

475 Spencer St
Melbourne VIC 3003

Phone   (03) 9329-7755
Freecall 1800-638-108
E-mail   *hotelspencer@hotkey.net.au*
Internet *www.hotelspencer.com*

City Scene Backpackers

361 Queensberry St
Melbourne North VIC 3051

Phone   (03) 9348-9525
Fax   (03) 9429-0492
E-mail   *cityscenebackpackers@yahoo.com.au*
Internet *www.cityscene.com.au*

Chapman Gardens YHA

76 Chapman St
Melbourne North VIC 3051

Phone   (03) 9328-3595
Fax   (03) 9329-7863
E-mail   *chapman@yhavic.org.au*
Internet *www.yha.org.au*

Queensberry Hill YHA

78 Howard St
Melbourne North VIC 3051

Phone (03) 9329-8599
Fax (03) 9326-8427
E-mail *queensberryhill@yhavic.org.au*
Internet *www.yha.org.au*

Nomads Market Inn

115 Cecil St
Melbourne South VIC 3205

Phone (03) 9690-2220
Fax (03) 9690-2544
Freecall 1800-241-445
E-mail *backpackers@marketinn.com.au*
Internet *www.marketinn.com.au*

Melbourne - Suburbs

Melbourne's suburbs are packed with culture, perhaps even more culture per square meter than in the city. Especially popular is the suburb of St Kilda, the center for groovy people and also home to the fun Luna Park. The main street offers a wide variety of shopping and dining experiences, including the famous specialty cake shops, and there's also a beach nearby. Prahran is more up-market and offers some of the best shopping experiences, at a price to match, while other areas are often interesting with their multi-cultural influences.

Carlton College Hostel

97 Drummond St
Carlton VIC 3053

Phone   (03) 9664-0664
Fax   (03) 9664-0680
Freecall 1800-066-551
E-mail   *backpackers@carltoncollege.com.au*
Internet *www.carltoncollege.com.au*

The Nunnery

116 Nicholson St
Fitzroy VIC 3065

Phone   (03) 9419-8637
Fax   (03) 9417-7736
Freecall 1800-032-635
E-mail   *infonunnery@bakpakgroup.com*
Internet *www.bakpakgroup.com/nunnery*

Gunn Island Brewbar

102 Canterbury Rd
Middle Park VIC 3206

Phone   (03) 9690-1958
Fax   (03) 9645-8928
E-mail   *gunnislandpub@ozemail.com.au*
Internet *www.gunnisland.com.au*

Lords Lodge Backpackers

204 Punt Rd
Prahran VIC 3181

Phone   (03) 9510-5658
Fax   (03) 9533-6663
E-mail   *lordslodge@bigpond.com*
Internet *www.lordslodge.com.au*

College Lawn Hotel

36 Greville St
Prahran VIC 3181

Phone   (03) 9510-6057
Fax   (03) 9510-7282
E-mail   *office@collegelawnhotel.com.au*
Internet *www.collegelawnhotel.com.au*

Richmond Hill Hotel

353 Church St
Richmond VIC 3121

Phone   (03) 9428-6501
Fax   (03) 9427-0128
Freecall 1800-801-618
E-mail   *rhhotel@bigpond.net.au*
Internet *www.richmondhillhotel.com.au*

Hotel Claremont

189 Toorak Rd
South Yarra VIC 3141

Phone   (03) 9826-8000
Fax   (03) 9827-8652
Freecall 1300-301-630
E-mail   *info@hotelclaremont.com*
Internet *www.hotelclaremont.com*

Ritz for Backpackers

169 Fitzroy St
St Kilda VIC 3182

Phone   (03) 9525-3501
Fax   (03) 9525-3863
Freecall 1800-670-364
E-mail   *ritz@backpackerscentre.com*
Internet *www.backpackerscentre.com*

Coffee Palace

24 Grey St
St Kilda VIC 3182

Phone   (03) 9534-5283
Fax   (03) 9593-9166
Freecall 1800-654-098
E-mail *Bookings@allnations.com.au*
Internet *www.backpackerscentre.com*

Enfield House

2 Enfield St
St Kilda VIC 3182

Phone   (03) 9534-8159
Fax   (03) 9534-5579
Freecall 1800-302-121
E-mail *infoenfield@bakpakgroup.com*
Internet *www.bakpakgroup.com/enfieldhouse*

The Oslo Hotel

38 Grey St
St Kilda VIC 3182

Phone   (03) 9525-4498
Fax   (03) 9530-0018
Freecall 1800-501-752
E-mail *backpackers_melb@oslohotel.com.au*
Internet *www.oslohotel.com.au*

Olembia
96 Barkly St
St Kilda VIC 3182

Phone   (03) 9537-1412
Fax   (03) 9537-1600
E-mail   *stay@olembia.com.au*
Internet *www.olembia.com.au*

Chapel Street Backpackers

22 Chapel St
Windsor VIC 3181

Phone   (03) 9533-6855
Fax   (03) 9533-6866
Freecall 1800-613-333
E-mail   *info@csbackpackers.com.au*
Internet *www.csbackpackers.com.au*

Pint on Punt

42 Punt Rd
Windsor VIC 3181

Phone   (03) 9510-4273
Fax   (03) 9529-5518
Freecall 1800-835-000
E-mail   *stkilda@pintonpunt.com.au*
Internet *www.pintonpunt.com.au*

Other Areas

Victoria's country-side has a wide range of different atmosphere's and activities. Unmissable is the Great Ocean Road, which runs west of Melbourne along the coast for around 300km. This is surely one of the most scenically beautiful stretches of road in the world. Apart from the pristine bays, cool towns, and National Parks, there is a series of incredible cliffs and rock formations with names such as the 12 Apostles, Loch Ard Gorge, and London Bridge.

Ballarat and Bendigo are both old gold-mining towns which offer the opportunity for you to try your hand at getting rich. Phillip Island is home to the famous daily 'Penguin Parade'. Mildura and other country areas here are good for finding harvesting work. And other areas such as Lakes Entrance and Halls Gap are renowned for their natural beauty.

Albury Motor Village YHA

372 Wagga Rd (Hume Highway), Lavington
Albury VIC 2641

Phone   (02) 6040-2999
Fax   (02) 6040-3160
E-mail *albury@yhavic.org.au*
Internet *www.yha.org.au*

Anglesea Backpackers

40 Noble St
Anglesea VIC 3230

Phone   (03) 5263-2664
E-mail *angleseabackpacker@iprimus.com.au*
Internet *home.iprimus.com.au/angleseabackpacker*

Sovereign Hill Lodge YHA

Magpie St
Ballarat VIC 3350

Phone   (03) 5333-3409
Fax   (03) 5333-5861
E-mail   *ballarat@yhavic.org.au*
Internet *www.yha.org.au*

Ironbark Bush Cabins

Watson St
Bendigo VIC 3550

Phone   (03) 5448-3344
Fax   (03) 5448-3787
Freecall 1800-737-378
E-mail   *ironbark@bendigos.net*
Internet *www.bwc.com.au/ironbark*

Bendigo YHA

33 Creek St South
Bendigo VIC 3550

Phone   (03) 5443-7680
Fax   (03) 5443-7687
E-mail   *bendigo@yhavic.org.au*
Internet *www.yha.org.au*

Bayplay Lodge

46 Canterbury Jetty Rd
Blairgowrie VIC 3942

Phone   (03) 5988-0188
Fax   (03) 5988-8032
E-mail   *bookings@bayplay.com.au*
Internet *www.bayplay.com.au*

Lakeside Leisure Resort YHA

Hutchinson's Rd
Bonnie Doon VIC 3720

Phone   (03) 5778-7252
Fax   (03) 5778-7569
E-mail   *bonniedoon@yhavic.org.au*
Internet *www.yha.org.au*

Bright Hikers Backpackers

Top Floor, 4 Ireland St
Bright VIC 3741

Phone   (03) 5750-1244
Fax   (03) 5750-1246
E-mail   *backpackers@brighthikers.com.au*
Internet *www.brighthikers.com.au*

Oasis Backpackers Nomads

410-424 High St
Echuca VIC 3564

Phone   (03) 5480-7866
Fax   (03) 5480-7867
Freecall 1800-613-333
E-mail   *nomads@river.net.au*
Internet *www.backpackersechuca.com*

Echuca Gardens YHA

103 Mitchell St
Echuca VIC 3564

Phone   (03) 5480-6522
E-mail   *echuca@yhavic.org.au*
Internet *www.yha.org.au*

McLeod Eco Farm

McLeod Rd
French Island VIC 3921

Phone   (03) 5678-0155
Fax   (03) 5678-0166
E-mail   *info@mcleodecofarm.com*
Internet *www.mcleodecofarm.com*

National Hotel

191 Moorabool St
Geelong VIC 3220

Phone   (03) 5229-1211
Fax   (03) 5227-0373
E-mail   *info@nationalhotel.com.au*
Internet *www.nationalhotel.com.au*

Karoonda Park YHA

Gelantipy Rd
Gelantipy VIC 3885

Phone   (03) 5155-0220
Fax   (03) 5155-0308
E-mail   *gelantipy@yhavic.org.au*
Internet *www.yha.org.au*

Brambuk Backpackers

Grampians Rd
Halls Gap VIC 3381

Phone   (03) 5356-4452
Fax   (03) 5356-4455
E-mail   *kayeharris@brambuk.com.au*
Internet *www.brambuk.com.au*

Grampians YHA Eco-Hostel

Corner Buckler St & Grampians Rd
Halls Gap VIC 3381

Phone (03) 5356-4544
Fax   (03) 5356-4543
E-mail *grampians@yhavic.org.au*
Internet *www.yha.org.au*

Wildwood YHA

42 Main Rd
Hepburn Springs VIC 3461

Phone (03) 5348-4435
Fax   (03) 5348-3555
E-mail *daylesford@yhavic.org.au*
Internet *www.mooltan.com.au*

Riviera Backpackers YHA

669-671 Esplanade
Lakes Entrance VIC 3909

Phone (03) 5155-2444
Fax   (03) 5155-4558
E-mail *lakesentrance@yhavic.org.au*
Internet *www.lakes-entrance.com/rivieraYHA*

Silver Sands Backpackers

33 Myer St
Lakes Entrance VIC 3909

Phone   (03) 5155-2343
Fax   (03) 5155-3134
E-mail   *manager@ssands.com.au*
Internet *www.ssands.com.au*

Great Ocean Road Backpackers YHA

10 Erskine Avenue
Lorne VIC 3232

Phone   (03) 5289-1809
Fax   (03) 5289-2508
E-mail   *lorne@yhavic.org.au*
Internet *www.yha.org.au*

Cambrai Backpackers Hostel

117 Johnson St
Maffra VIC 3860

Phone   (03) 5147-1600
Fax   (03) 5147-3175
Freecall 1800-101-113
E-mail   *cambrai@netspace.net.au*
Internet *www.southeasthostel.com*

Riverboat Bungalow

27 Chaffey Avenue
Mildura VIC 3500

Phone   (03) 5021-5315
Fax   (03) 5023-0984
E-mail   *bungalow@vic.ozland.net.au*
Internet users.mildura.net.au/bungalow

Juicy Grape International

Block 446, Calder Hwy, Sunnycliffs
Mildura VIC 3500

Phone   (03) 5024-2112
E-mail   *james@juicygrape.com*
Internet www.juicygrape.com

Mildura International Backpackers

5 Cedar Avenue
Mildura VIC 3500

Phone   (03) 5021-0133
E-mail   *mibpackers@hotmail.com*

YHA Lodge

The Avenue
Mount Buller VIC 3723

Phone   (03) 5777-6181
Fax   (03) 5777-6691
E-mail *mountbuller@yhavic.org.au*
Internet *www.ciau.com.au/YHA/buller.htm*

Amaroo Park YHA

97 Church St, Cowes
Phillip Island VIC 3922

Phone   (03) 5952-2548
Fax   (03) 5952-3620
E-mail *phillipisland@yhavic.org.au*
Internet *www.yha.org.au*

Port Campbell YHA

18 Tregea St
Port Campbell VIC 3269

Phone   (03) 5598-6305
Fax   (03) 5598-6305
E-mail *portcampbell@yhavic.org.au*
Internet *www.yha.org.au*

Port Fairy YHA

8 Cox St
Port Fairy VIC 3284

Phone   (03) 5568-2468
Fax   (03) 5568-2302
E-mail   *portfairy@yhavic.org.au*
Internet *www.yha.org.au*

The Queenscliff Inn YHA

59 Hesse St
Queenscliff VIC 3225

Phone   (03) 5258-3737
Fax   (03) 5258-3737
E-mail   *queenscliff@yhavic.org.au*
Internet *www.yha.org.au*

Sorrento YHA

3 Miranda St
Sorrento VIC 3943

Phone   (03) 5984-4323
Fax   (03) 5984-2430
E-mail   *sorrento@yhavic.org.au*
Internet *www.yha.org.au*

Australian Bush Settlement

Maroondah Highway
Taggerty VIC 3714

Phone   (03) 5774-7378
Fax   (03) 5774-7442
E-mail   *bushlife@virtual.net.au*
Internet
www.green.net.au/australian_bush_settlement

Bell's Beach Backpackers

51-53 Surfcoast Highway
Torquay VIC 3228

Phone   (03) 5261-7070
Fax   (03) 5261-3879
Freecall 1800-737-378
E-mail   *anthony@bellsbeachbackpackers.com.au*
Internet *www.bellsbeachbackpackers.com.au*

Point Break Backpackers

185 Addiscott Rd
Torquay VIC 3228

Phone   (03) 5261-5105
Fax   (03) 5261-3123
E-mail   *pt_break@yahoo.com.au*
Internet *www.pointbreakbackpackers.com.au*

Wangaratta Backpackers

Old Hume Highway
Wangaratta North VIC 3676

Phone   (03) 5721-2624
Fax   (03) 5722-4020
E-mail   *fammotel@netc.net.au*

Warnambool Beach Backpackers

17 Stanley St
Warrnambool VIC 3280

Phone   (03) 5562-4874
Fax   (03) 5562-4874
E-mail   *johnpearson@hotmail.com*

Eumeralla Backpackers

High St
Yambuk VIC 3285

Phone   (03) 5568-4204
Fax   (03) 5567-1298
E-mail   *fram@standard.net.au*
Internet *www.backpacker.faithweb.com*

Western Australia (WA)

Western Australia occupies almost a third of the land of Australia and is the size of India! Perth is the capital and is a great place to relax, as is the nearby town of Freo, both of which have great surfing, great people and great atmosphere.

South of Perth is some of the best surfing in the world, along with an abundance of beautiful natural attractions. The central coast above Perth has the incredible Monkey Mia with it's daily dolphin visitors, and a little further north brings to you to Ningaloo Reef, a place to rival the Great Barrier Reef on the east coast and also more accessible. In the far north there's the unique beauty of Broome and the nearby Kimberleys.

A lot of travelers remark after visiting the remote and isolated west coast - 'Now this is the real Australia'. The whole of Western Australia is a gem waiting to be discovered - don't miss it.

Perth

Perth is Western Australia's capital, and it's a great place to kick-back and relax. The people are friendly, the food is good, the surf is up, and the weather is great - Perth has more sunny days per year than any other capital.

City & Surf Backpackers

41 Money St
Perth WA 6000

Phone   (08) 9227-1234
Fax   (08) 9227-1941
E-mail   *email@backpacker.com.au*
Internet *www.backpacker.com.au*

Globe Hostel

497 Wellington St
Perth WA 6000

Phone   (08) 9321-4080
Fax   (08) 9226-3202
E-mail   *info@globebackpackers.com.au*
Internet *www.globebackpackers.com.au*

Cheviot International Lodge

30 Bulwer St
Perth WA 6000

Phone   (08) 9227-6817
Fax   (08) 9227-6826
Freecall 1800-356-346
E-mail   *Cheviot_Intl@hotmail.com*
Internet *www.members.tripod.com/cheviotlodge*

12:01 East Backpackers

195 Hay St
Perth WA 6000

Phone   (08) 9221-1666
Fax   (08) 9221-1662
Freecall 1800-001-201
E-mail   *backpackers1201east@hotmail.com*
Internet *www.touch88.com.au/~east1201*

Exclusive Backpackers

158 Adelaide Terrace
Perth WA 6000

Phone   (08) 9221-9991
E-mail   *exclusivebackpackers@hotmail.com*
Internet *www.exclusivebackpackers.com*

Murray Street Hostel

119 Murray St
Perth WA 6000

Phone   (08) 9325-7627
Fax   (08) 9221-0083
E-mail   *backpackers@murrayst.com*
Internet *www.murrayst.com*

North Lodge Backpackers

225 Beaufort St
Perth WA 6000

Phone   (08) 9227-7588
Fax   (08) 9227-5558
E-mail   *northlodge@hotmail.com*
Internet *www.northlodge-perthwa.com*

Grand Central Backpackers

379 Wellington St
Perth WA 6000

Phone   (08) 9421-1123
Fax   (08) 9421-1650
E-mail   *grandcentralbp@hotmail.com*

Britannia International YHA

253 William St
Perth WA 6003

Phone   (08) 9328-6121
Fax   (08) 9227-9784
E-mail   *britannia@yhawa.com.au*
Internet *www.yha.org.au*

Rainbow Lodge

133 Summers St
Perth East WA 6004

Phone   (08) 9227-1818
E-mail   *Ron@rainbowlodge.com.au*
Internet *www.rainbowlodge.com.au*

Club Red Backpackers

494-496 Newcastle St
Perth West WA 6005

Phone   (08) 9227-9969
Fax   (08) 9227-9085
Freecall 1800-679-969
E-mail   *info@club-red.com.au*
Internet *www.redbackpackers.com.au*

Beatty Lodge

235 Vincent St
Perth West WA 6005

Phone   (08) 9227-1521
Fax   (08) 9227-6509
E-mail   *info@beattylodge.com.au*
Internet *www.beattylodge.com.au*

Perth - Northbridge

Northbridge is just 5 minutes from Perth's city center, and is the focus of entertainment in Perth, offering restaurants, parties, socializing and nightlife.

Coolibah Lodge

194 Brisbane St
Northbridge WA 6000

Phone   (08) 9328-9958
Fax   (08) 9227-6231
E-mail   *mail@coolibahlodge.com.au*
Internet *www.coolibahlodge.com.au*

Spinner's Backpackers

342 Newcastle St
Northbridge WA 6000

Phone   (08) 9328-9468
Fax   (08) 9228-2917
E-mail *spinners2@hotmail.com*
Internet *www.ic-net.com.au/~spinners*

Ozi Inn

282 Newcastle St
Northbridge WA 6000

Phone   (08) 9328-1222
E-mail *info@oziinn.com*
Internet *www.oziinn.com*

The Witch's Hat

148 Palmerston St
Northbridge WA 6000

Phone   (08) 9228-4228
Fax   (08) 9228-4229
Freecall 1800-818-358
E-mail *reservations@witchs-hat.com*
Internet *www.witchs-hat.com*

Billabong Backpackers Resort

381 Beaufort St
Northbridge WA 6003

Phone   (08) 9328-7720
Fax   (08) 9328-7721
E-mail   *bookings@billabongresort.com.au*
Internet *www.billabongresort.com.au*

Shiralee Backpackers Hostel

107 Brisbane St
Northbridge WA 6003

Phone   (08) 9227-7448
Fax   (08) 9227-7446
Freecall 1800-227-745
E-mail   *info@shiralee.com.au*
Internet *www.shiralee.com.au*

Northbridge YHA Backpackers

46 Francis St
Northbridge WA 6003

Phone   (08) 9328-7794
Fax   (08) 9328-7794
E-mail   *northbridge@yhawa.com.au*
Internet *www.yha.org.au*

Governor Robinsons

7 Robinson Avenue
Northbridge WA 6003

Phone   (08) 9328-3200
Fax   (08) 9328-3211
E-mail   *info@govrobinsons.com.au*
Internet *www.govrobinsons.com.au*

Mad Cat Backpackers

55-63 Stirling St
Northbridge WA 6003

Phone   (08) 9228-4966
Fax   (08) 9227-7785
E-mail   *madcat@madcatbackpackers.com.au*
Internet *www.madcatbackpackers.com.au*

Underground Backpackers

268 Newcastle St
Northbridge WA 6004

Phone   (08) 9228-3755
Fax   (08) 9228-3744
Freecall 1800-033-089
E-mail   *info@undergroundbackpackers.com.au*
Internet *www.undergroundbackpackers.com.au*

Perth - Beaches

Perth's beaches offer some of the best surfing of any capital, and the sunsets here over the ocean are beautiful.

City & Surf Backpackers

119 Scarborough Beach Rd
Scarborough WA 6019

Phone   (08) 9227-1234
Fax   (08) 9227-1941
E-mail *email@backpacker.com.au*
Internet *www.backpacker.com.au*

West Beach Lagoon

251 West Coast Highway
Scarborough WA 6019

Phone   (08) 9341-6122
Fax   (08) 9341-5944
Freecall 1800-999-339
E-mail *info@westbeachlagoon.com.au*
Internet *www.westbeachlagoon.com.au*

Indigo Surf Lodge

256 West Coast Highway
Scarborough WA 6019

Phone   (08) 9245-3388
Fax   (08) 9245-5588
E-mail *indigo_netcafe@hotmail.com*
Internet *www.indigonet.com.au*

Western Beach Lodge

6 Westborough St
Scarborough WA 6019

Phone   (08) 9245-1624
E-mail westernbeach@iprimus.com.au

Mandarin Gardens

20 - 28 Wheatcroft St
Scarborough WA 6019

Phone   (08) 9341-5431
Fax   (08) 9245-1553
E-mail *madarinwa@bigpond.com*
Internet *www.mandarinwa.com*

Ocean Beach Backpackers

Corner Marine Parade & Eric St
Cottesloe WA 6011

Phone   (08) 9384-5111
Fax   (08) 9384-5222
E-mail   *backpackers@obh.com.au*
Internet *www.obh.com.au/backpackers*

Fremantle (Freo)

Fremantle is less than 30 minutes from Perth and is a cool town with European architecture and a 'happening vibe'. Markets, beaches, trendy shops, the 'Cappucino Strip' and alfresco dining all make this a great place to stay.

Redback Portcity Pirates Backpackers

11 Essex St
Freemantle WA 6160

Phone   (08) 9335-6635
E-mail   *freopirates@hotmail.com*
Internet *www.planetbackpack.com*

Cheviot Marina Backpackers

Corner Beach & Parry Sts
Fremantle WA 6160

Phone   (08) 9433-2055
Fax   (08) 9433-2066
Freecall 1800-255-644
E-mail   *cheviotmarina@hotmail.com*
Internet *www.members.tripod.com/cheviotlodge*

Old Firestation Backpackers

18 Phillimore St
Fremantle WA 6160

Phone   (08) 9430-5454
Fax   (08) 9335-6828
E-mail   *firestation@firestation.fdns.net*
Internet *www.old-firestation.net*

Sundancer Backpackers Resort

80 High St
Fremantle WA 6160

Phone   (08) 9336-6080
Freecall 1800-061-144
E-mail   *sundancer_resort@tpg.com.au*
Internet *www.sundancer-resort.com.au*

South-West WA

The area south of Perth is rapidly growing in popularity with backpackers, and all these towns offer their own attractions and activities. There are plentiful beaches along here, many such as Margaret River renowned for having some of the best surf in the world. Inland are interesting national parks, caves and goldfields, and more.

Albany Backpackers

Corner Stirling Terrace & Spencer St
Albany WA 6330

Phone   (08) 9841-8848
Fax   (08) 9841-8848
Freecall 1800-644-088
E-mail   *abp@albanybackpackers.com.au*
Internet *www.albanybackpackers.com.au*

Bayview YHA

49 Duke St
Albany WA 6330

Phone   (08) 9842-3388
Fax   (08) 9841-3949
E-mail   *albany@yhawa.com.au*
Internet *www.yha.org.au*

Baywatch Manor Resort YHA

88 Blackwood Avenue
Augusta WA 6290

Phone   (08) 9758-1290
Fax   (08) 9758-1291
E-mail *enquiries@baywatchmanor.com.au*
Internet *www.baywatchmanor.com.au*

Balingup Backpackers Eco Lodge

26 Brockman St
Balingup WA 6253

Phone   (08) 9764-1049
Fax   (08) 9764-1049
E-mail *hotbunks@wn.com.au*
Internet *www.wn.com.au/hotbunks*

Wander Inn - Bunbury Backpackers YHA

Dolphin City, 16 Clifton St
Bunbury WA 6230

Phone   (08) 9721-3242
Fax   (08) 9721-3242
E-mail *wanderinnbp@yahoo.com*
Internet *www.yha.org.au*

Busselton Backpackers

14 Peel Terrace
Busselton WA 6280

Phone   (08) 9754-2763
E-mail   *backpackers@bsnbpk.com*
Internet *www.bsnbpk.com*

Blue Wren Backpackers

17 Prince St
Denmark WA 6333

Phone   (08) 9848-3300
E-mail   *blue.wren@bigpond.com*
Internet bluewren.batcave.net

Denmark Waterfront

63 Inlet Drive
Denmark WA 6333

Phone   (08) 9848-1147
Fax   (08) 9848-1965
E-mail   *holiday@denmarkwaterfront.com.au*
Internet *www.denmarkwaterfront.com.au*

Nomads Railway Hotel

58 South West Highway
Donnybrook WA 6239

Phone   (08) 9731-1013
Fax   (08) 9731-2111
E-mail   *railway@starwan.com.au*
Internet *www.nomadsworld.com/oz*

Dunsborough Inn

50 Dunn Bay Rd
Dunsborough WA 6281

Phone   (08) 9756-7277
Fax   (08) 9756-7377
E-mail   *dunsinn@wn.com.au*
Internet *www.dunsboroughinn.com*

Three Pines Beach YHA

201-205 Geographe Bay Rd, Quindalup
Dunsborough WA 6281

Phone   (08) 9755-3107
Fax   (08) 9755-3028
E-mail   *dunsboroughyha@hotmail.com*
Internet *www.yha.org.au*

Blue Waters Lodge YHA

299 Goldfields Rd
Esperance WA 6450

Phone   (08) 9071-1040
Fax   (08) 9071-1040
E-mail   *yhaesperance@hotmail.com*
Internet *www.yha.org.au*

Margaret River Lodge YHA

220 Railway Terrace
Margaret River WA 6285

Phone   (08) 9757-9532
Fax   (08) 9757-2532
E-mail   *stay@mrlodge.com.au*
Internet *www.mrlodge.com.au*

Surf Point Resort

Riedle Drive, Gnarabup Beach
Margaret River WA 6285

Phone   (08) 9757-1777
Fax   (08) 9757-1077
Freecall 1800-071-777
E-mail   *office@surfpoint.com.au*
Internet *www.surfpoint.com.au*

Inne Town Backpackers

93 Bussell Highway
Margaret River WA 6285

Phone   (08) 9757-3698
Fax   (08) 9757-3122
Freecall 1800-244-115
E-mail   *innetown@bigpond.com*

Smiffy's Margaret River Retreat

343 Bussell Highway
Margaret River WA 6286

Phone   (08) 9757-7419
Fax   (08) 9757-7419
E-mail   *smiffys@highway1.com.au*
Internet *www.perth-wa.com/cape/accom/smiffy*

Walpole Backpackers

Lot 131, Corner Pier St & Park Avenue
Walpole WA 6398

Phone   (08) 9840-1244
Fax   (08) 9840-1244
E-mail   *walpolebackpackers@bigpond.com*
Internet *www.walpolebackpackers.com*

Central Coast

The central coast offers some very interesting natural attractions. Monkey Mia is one of the few places in the world where you can interact with a pod of wild dolphins that visit the beach every day to meet with humans. Exmouth and other nearby towns offer snorkeling and diving access to the Ningaloo Reef, which can be easily accessed by just wading out from the beach, unlike the Great Barrier Reef on the east coast which usually requires a boat trip. You can also swim here with giant harmless whale sharks. There are many other attractions here such as the famous rock formation known as Pinnacles, near the town of Cervantes.

Pinnacles Beach Backpackers

91 Seville St
Cervantes WA 6511

Phone   (08) 9652-7377
Fax   (08) 9652-7318
Freecall 1800-245-232
E-mail   *pbb@wn.com.au*
Internet *www.wn.com.au/pbbackpackers*

Chapman Valley Farm Backpackers

Murphy Norris Rd, Yetna
Chapman Valley WA 6532

Phone   (08) 9920-5034
Fax   (08) 9920-5229
E-mail   *claudia@modnet.com.au*
Internet redhill.modnet.com.au

Ningaloo Club

French St
Coray Bay WA 6701

Phone   (08) 9948-5100
Fax   (08) 9385-7413
E-mail   *bcb@coralbaywa.com*
Internet *www.ningalooclub.com*

Bay Lodge YHA

95 Knight Terrace
Denham WA 6537

Phone   (08) 9948-1278
Fax   (08) 9948-1031
E-mail   *baylodge@wn.com.au*
Internet *www.yha.org.au*

Dongara Backpackers YHA

32 Waldeck St
Dongara WA 6525

Phone   (08) 9927-1581
Fax   (08) 9927-1592
E-mail   *dongarabackpack@westnet.com.au*
Internet *www.yha.org.au*

Pete's Exmouth Backpackers YHA

Corner of Truscott Crescent & Murat Rd
Exmouth WA 6707

Phone   (08) 9949-1101
Fax   (08) 9949-1402
Freecall 1800-621-101
E-mail   *exmouthvillage@nwc.net.au*
Internet *www.exmouthvillage.com*

Exmouth Base Lodge

Murat Rd
Exmouth WA 6707

Phone   (08) 9949-1474
Fax   (08) 9949-1440
Freecall 1800-241-474
E-mail   *baselodge@nwc.net.au*

Winstons Backpackers

Murat Rd
Exmouth WA 6707

Phone   (08) 9949-2377
Fax   (08) 9949-2577
E-mail   *info@exmouthresort.com*
Internet *www.exmouthresort.com*

Marina Beach Retreat

50 Market St
Exmouth WA 6707

Phone   (08) 9949-1500
Fax   (08) 9949-1500
E-mail *chasetours@ningaloochase.com.au*
Internet *www.ningaloochase.com.au*

Foreshore Backpackers YHA

172 Marine Terrace
Geraldton WA 6530

Phone   (08) 9921-3275
Fax   (08) 9921-3233
E-mail *foreshorebp@hotmail.com*
Internet *www.yha.org.au*

Rock Lobster Lodge YHA

51 Mortimer St
Kalbarri WA 6536

Phone   (08) 9937-1430
Fax   (08) 9937-1563
E-mail *kalbarribackpackers@wn.com.au*
Internet *www.yha.org.au*

Lancelin Lodge YHA

10 Hopkins St
Lancelin WA 6044

Phone   (08) 9655-2020
Fax   (08) 9655-2021
E-mail   *lanlodge@windspeed.net.au*
Internet *www.lancelinlodge.com.au*

Monkey Mia Dolphin Resort YHA

Monkey Mia Rd
Monkey Mia, Shark Bay WA 6537

Phone   (08) 9948-1320
Fax   (08) 9948-1034
Freecall 1800-653-611
E-mail   *sales@monkeymia.com.au*
Internet *www.monkeymia.com.au*

North WA

It's a long trip to the far north of Western Australia, and everyone who goes there agrees - it's well worth the journey. Broome is the biggest city in the region, and is home to the famous and beautiful Cable Beach which is popularly visited on the back of a camel! Broome and Kununurra are gateways to the Kimberley region with it's beautiful Gorges and other-worldly desert landscapes, as well as being great places to learn about the ancient Aboriginal culture.

Kimberley Klub

Frederick St
Broome WA 6725

Phone   (08) 9192-3233
Fax   (08) 9192-3530
E-mail   *info@kimberleyklub.com*
Internet *www.kimberleyklub.com*

Broome's Last Resort YHA

2 Bagot St
Broome WA 6725

Phone   (08) 9193-5000
Fax   (08) 9193-6033
E-mail   *lastresortyha@smartchat.net.au*
Internet *www.yha.org.au*

Buccaneer Cove

via Derby or Broome
Cockatoo Island WA

Phone   (08) 9191-7477
Fax   (08) 9191-7484
E-mail   *info@cockatooisland.com*
Internet *www.cockatooisland.com*

Karratha Backpackers

110 Wellard Way
Karratha WA 6714

Phone   (08) 9144-4904
E-mail   *backpackers@kisser.net.au*
Internet *www.kisser.net.au/backpackers*

Kununurra Backpackers Adventure Centre

22 Nutwood Crescent
Kununurra WA 6743

Phone   (08) 9169-1998
Fax   (08) 9168-3998
Freecall 1800-641-998
E-mail   *backpack@adventure.kimberley.net.au*
Internet *www.adventure.kimberley.net.au*

Desert Inn 'Backpackers Oasis' YHA

124 Konkerberry Drive
Kununurra WA 6743

Phone   (08) 9168-2702
Fax   (08) 9168-2271
Freecall 1800-805-010
E-mail   *kimberleybookings@wn.com.au*
Internet *www.kimberleyadventure.com*

Dingo's Oasis Backpackers

59 Kingsmill St
Port Hedland WA 1234

Phone   (08) 9173-1000
Fax   (08) 9173-5149
E-mail   *dingos@dingotrek.com.au*
Internet *www.dingotrek.com.au*

Printed in the United Kingdom
by Lightning Source UK Ltd.
116269UKS00001B/361-363